EASY
ECO
AUDITING

EASY ECO AUDITING

How to make your home and workplace planet-friendly

Donnachadh McCarthy

GAIA
THINKING

For Pauline, Ruth, Joe, Liz and Nick for being patient, supportive and loving friends.

An Hachette Livre UK Company

First published in Great Britain in 2008 by
Gaia, a division of Octopus Publishing Group Ltd
2–4 Heron Quays, London E14 4JP
www.octopusbooks.co.uk

ISBN 978-1-85675-293-0

A CIP catalogue record for this book is available from
the British Library

Printed and bound in Italy

Printed on Cyclus Offset, a 100 per cent recycled paper

10 9 8 7 6 5 4 3 2 1

Note
The authors and publisher cannot accept liability for any loss or
damage incurred as a result (directly or indirectly) of the advice
or information contained in this book or the use or application
of the contents of this book.

Prices are only given in British Pounds because the conversion
rate between British Pounds and Euros fluctuates. All prices are
accurate at the time of compilation but are liable to change.

Contents

Introduction

A clear, positive vision underpins this book. The aim is to enable you to carry out a basic eco-audit of your home and your workplace, and so join the millions of others across the world who are already taking action to save our environment and lessen the effects of the climate crisis brought about by a dangerous build-up of greenhouse gases.

Climate change

There is no doubt that the current consumer and oil-addicted lifestyles of so many of the six billion humans living on this planet are destroying huge sections of the natural world, with all its glorious beauty, and causing catastrophic changes to the climate. Even senior economists are saying that this is the greatest threat we have ever faced, and the threat extends beyond our human way of life to the future of the thousands of other organisms with which we share the earth. The scale of the crisis dwarfs the two world wars and the Great Depression put together, but this time our political leaders seem to be in denial, taking no meaningful steps to rein in soaring carbon dioxide (CO_2) emissions, which are the root cause of climate change. Even worse, while they profess to be concerned, their policies promote ever more fossil-fuel-based industrialization.

Sir Nicholas Stern, a former economist with the World Bank, was asked by the UK government to review the economic implications of climate change. His 2006 report laid out the case for reducing emissions now to avoid a 2°C rise in temperature. Even a rise of 2°C, he suggested, could result in the loss of up to 30 per cent of species; a rise of over 2°C could result in the Amazon rainforest being turned into a vast savannah. The concomitant release of millions of tonnes of carbon dioxide stored in its trees could lead to temperatures rising above 3°C, which in turn could lead to the melting of the permafrost within the Arctic Circle, which would release billions of tonnes of methane, leading to temperatures potentially rising above 4°C. This could result in further heating of the oceans and the possible release of billions of tonnes of methane salts buried on the seabed, which would lead to runaway, irreversible global scorching and the end of life as we know it. A UK parliamentary report released in August 2007 included evidence from the Tyndall Centre for Climate Change Research that with current government policies there was a 92 to 100 per cent chance of global warming increasing by 2°C and a 50 per cent chance of it increasing by 4°C. Stern was right. This is an unimaginable crisis and requires urgent action now from all of us, including our politicians.

Unfortunately, politicians will only take the actions necessary to tackle the climate crisis if they feel they have a mandate from the public and business to do so. To date, it is not clear that such a mandate exists. It is up to us to create an unstoppable but gentle eco-revolution among ordinary householders, employees and businesspeople. This book provides a blueprint for the green revolution that each and every one of us can take part in, at home and at work. At the heart of this eco-revolution is the simple tool of eco-auditing, through which individuals can eco-revolutionize their houses, the houses of other people in their streets and communities, and their workplaces, slashing levels of the emissions and waste that are contributing to our current crisis. This book shows ordinary people of all ages, races and walks of life who are not so-called 'environmental experts' how to eco-audit effectively. The more of us who do this, the faster society at large will feel that they can authorize our elected politicians to put in place the wider regulatory and legislative framework needed to deal with climate change.

What is eco-auditing?

Eco-auditing is the process of assessing the current eco-friendliness of a home or business and recommending ways it can be improved. Easy-to-use tools show how that improvement can be measured year by year. This book provides the basic beginners' eco-auditing guide, whether you are a parent or a student at home or a chief executive or a cleaner at work. It analyses the basic structure of an eco-audit for both the home and the workplace, examining how to calculate energy carbon footprints and find ways to address all the various other environmental problems, from water use to waste disposal.

Becoming green

Everyone has their own story of how they woke up to the seriousness of the threat to the environment. If you are reading this book, then in all likelihood you are already aware of the threat. In my work, I have recently met many people in business for whom the Al Gore movie *An Inconvenient Truth* was their wake-up call. The process of greening my own life started in 1992 when I found myself, through one of those strange twists of fate, on a visit to the Yanomami Indians in the heart of the Amazonian rainforest. Up until that time, I had not paid any attention to what was happening to the environment around me. I was too busy focused on my then career as a freelance ballet dancer. I had studied at the Irish National Ballet, worked with the Dublin City Ballet and, at the time of the trip to the Amazon, was enjoying performing at the Royal Opera House, Covent Garden.

A trip to a remote rainforest would never have occurred to me – I am not at heart a natural jungle explorer! But when Linda Mutch and Brian Melville, the homeopath and acupuncturist who used to treat my dance injuries, invited me to join a group of alternative practitioners to visit the Yanomami Indians in the border area between Venezuela and Brazil, I gulped and said yes. Little did I realize that that snap decision was going to change my life completely, leading to involvement in national politics and eventually my current career as an eco-auditor and media environmentalist.

The Yanomami had lived for thousands of years in the forest without destroying it. I witnessed at first hand the destruction of their forest and also the destruction of other local indigenous people's way of life, as the bulldozers of Western consumers moved ever closer. While the Yanomami did not want Westerners coming to disrupt their way of life, they generously invited me to join their tribe. Instead, I resolved to return to London and do what I could to stop Britain's consumerist lifestyle from being so destructive to the planet and our fellow human beings. At the time, I was not aware that our destruction of their trees was not the only overwhelming threat to these innocent people; but in the following years I learned to my horror that our carbon emissions were potentially leading to the death of the entire forest as the global climate crisis escalates.

Back in my flat in Camberwell, I decided the best place to start was my own lifestyle. Not having much money at the time – freelance ballet dancers do not exactly make a fortune – I decided to buy at least one item of organic food every time I went to a supermarket. Thus my first step was to buy a bottle of Good Earth organic tomato ketchup. The next and most important step was taking the Earth Summit Pledge. This was drawn up by international environmental charities in advance of the 1992 Earth Summit of world leaders in Rio de Janeiro and committed those who took the pledge to turn off the heating and lighting in rooms that they were leaving empty. It is now so deeply ingrained in my subconscious that I am almost physically unable to leave a room without turning the lights off. I cannot emphasize strongly enough how this is one of the most important aspects of greening your lifestyle. It can be more important than any wind turbine or solar panel. Eliminating profligate wastage is the cheapest, fastest and most effective way we have of slashing our carbon and environmental footprints.

In addition to adopting a more eco-friendly lifestyle, I wanted to make my home into a retro eco-home. In other words, I wanted as much of the heat, light and water that I still needed, after I had started eliminating waste, to be provided in as eco-friendly a way as possible, even though I lived in an 1840s end of terrace house in the heart of London. Over the next 15 years I gradually undertook a major eco-renovation of my home, installing rain-harvesting systems and solar panels, insulating and reducing waste to the point where I am now a net exporter of electricity to the national grid. This year, really excitingly, for the first time the carbon dioxide saved by the electricity sold to the national grid exceeded that emitted by the gas I imported for cooking and heating. This has made mine one of the first climate-positive homes in London. The full story of how I achieved this is given in Chapter 11 (see pages 249–61).

Environmental campaigning and politics

Following my return, I also started getting involved in wider environmental campaigns. I am a member of Survival International, Greenpeace and Friends of the Earth. I was a director of the environmental charity Groundwork Southwark for the last 12 years. My first step was to lead a successful campaign to stop a local wildlife site in Burgess Park, near my home, being built on. This was the first of over 40 successful campaigns to stop various sections of this inner London park being built on.

As a result of my involvement with the park campaign, I got into local politics, joining the Liberal Democrats, and was soon elected as a councillor representing the Aylesbury Estate in inner London. I managed to introduce ground-breaking policies for the time – this was the mid-1990s – requiring composting, cycle storage and rain barrels on all new properties and pioneered the council's Pesticide Reduction Strategy, which was the first of its kind in the UK and won a Green Apple Award. I also persuaded the council to carry out their first environmental audit of a major new quarter-of-a-billion-pound housing redevelopment in Peckham, which led to significant improvements, including the implementation of affordable warmth standards of insulation and the installation of water efficiency appliances.

I stood for election to the party's national executive, won and spent most of the following seven years on the executive. I was a member of national policy committees concerned with a range of issues, including defence, globalization, GM crops, renewable energy and rural affairs. I had the privilege of getting more individual policies and motions through conference than any other member at the time. These included proposals to end the practice of parliamentarians acting as professional political lobbyists, committing the party to electing its nominees to the Lords, having an annual environmental audit, declaring our political donations, promoting renewable energy as part of our rural affairs policy, leading by example on reducing nuclear weapons and protecting non-GM crops from contamination by GM pollen.

In 2002, to my astonishment, I was elected as the deputy chair of the party's federal executive. I was re-elected for a second term a year later. This helped enormously in getting the eco-audit of the party headquarters implemented and during this time the environmental performance of party HQ improved dramatically. However, despite my success in getting significant chunks of policy adopted democratically at party conference, they were not supported by the leadership or included in the manifesto. I saw for myself the influence of lobbyists from the oil, mining and tax-haven industries and watched as many of the initiatives I had successfully piloted were thwarted. I grew increasingly frustrated with aspects of the party political process and resigned in 2004.

One enormously positive lesson this experience of national politics taught me is that politicians frequently follow rather than lead public opinion. Another is that an economy's vested financial interests will nearly always be more powerful politically than the democratic process. I now believe that, in order to tackle the climate crisis with the extreme urgency it requires, we need to move public opinion and to change buying habits so that politicians will be forced by economics to enact the environmental regulations required. I therefore decided to leave politics and to create a career instead as a media environmentalist.

I was lucky in being commissioned to write my first book, *Saving the Planet Without Costing the Earth*, by Sheena Dewan of Vision Paperbacks around this time. It was to be a guide on how to live an eco-friendly lifestyle, based on my own experiences over the previous ten years. Its success opened the door to the media that I needed for my new vision and over the last three years I have had the privilege of doing about five media interviews a week for TV, radio stations and newspapers around the world, on a huge range of environmental issues. It has also opened up a career as a freelance eco-journalist and I now have my own weekly eco-column in the *Independent* newspaper, which enables me to provide practical advice on how people can take effective action in their own day-to-day lives. My aim is to help make a personal and work eco-lifestyle both desirable and fashionable, while making a lifestyle that recklessly wastes the planet's resources something that is antisocial. I want people to feel proud of their low carbon footprint and embarrassed about their gas-guzzling urban 4x4s. I want to recast the Second World War slogan 'Careless talk costs lives' as 'Wasting energy costs lives' or, to put it positively, 'Saving energy saves lives!'

3 Acorns Eco-Audits

Following the publication in 2004 of my book, ordinary householders and businesses started coming to me and asking for help in making their homes and businesses more eco-friendly. This was how I started my 3 Acorns Eco-Audits consultancy. It is a privilege to get into the nitty-gritty of how a family or company operates in relation to their impact on the environment and it has been both hugely rewarding and a marvellous learning experience. Seeing and hearing what is actually happening in people's homes and businesses means that when I am writing about eco-issues or doing interviews I am speaking from real-life experiences rather than theoretically.

Politicians cannot take action on our climate crisis if they do not have permission from the people or the vested financial interests that rule our economy. The more of us who are actually getting on with greening our own homes and businesses, the sooner the government will feel it has a mandate to act decisively. Eco-auditing has a crucial role in helping to create that political mandate.

Why we need a gentle eco-revolution

Before we get into the detail of how to carry out an eco-audit or how to calculate an energy carbon footprint, it is worth reminding ourselves why we need to cut the environmental impact of our families and work colleagues.

• The burning of coal, gas and oil is causing the planet's temperature to rise, threatening climate chaos across the globe.

• The consumption of food and especially meat by over six billion people is leading to the destruction of much of our remaining unspoilt wildernesses.

• The indiscriminate felling of the remaining ancient tropical rain and temperate forests is leading to the extinction of thousands of species.

• The over-consumption of water is leading to water scarcity for millions of people across the developed and developing worlds.

• The emission of a plethora of untested artificial chemicals is threatening the health of humans and wildlife worldwide.

• Our over-consumption and wastage of the earth's finite natural resources such as fossil fuels, minerals and soil mean that future generations will not be able to enjoy their benefits.

• The waste mountains created by consumer lifestyles are polluting our soil and waterways.

• The abuse of antibiotics in farming and for non-clinical uses and the manipulation of genetics threaten our future health and food security.

• The nuclear waste from power stations and nuclear weapons programmes is leaving a hugely expensive and dangerous radioactive legacy for generations to come.

• The world's population is projected to rise to over nine billion people by 2050, exacerbating all of the above crises even further.

Good news

When you start thinking about these problems, the temptation is to feel overwhelmed and wonder if it is worth doing anything in our own home and work lives. However, while nature is increasingly sending out terrifying alarm signals, some good news is beginning to emerge. There is no doubt that an absolute explosion of awareness about environmental issues in general and the climate crisis in particular has taken place over the last three years. But in my experience the real wake-up call was Hurricane Katrina, which devastated New Orleans in August 2005, leaving thousands dead in its wake and the city submerged under 6 metres of floodwaters.

To many in the West, the consequences of the climate crisis up until then had been remote, something that affected faraway areas such as Alaskan forests or isolated Pacific islands. Seeing a modern city brought to its knees, with thousands of people at the mercy of nature and the emergency infrastructure hopelessly inadequate to deal with the scale of the assault, changed that forever. Scientists now accept that the doubling of hurricanes and tropical storms over the last century is due to the warming of the Atlantic and Caribbean seas. Warmer seas lead to more powerful and frequent hurricanes. So whether or not the destructive power of Katrina was directly attributable to the heating seas did not detract from the demonstration of what the near-future will hold if scientific predictions of stronger and more frequent hurricanes resulting from climate change actually manifest themselves. As a result, millions of people since then have started to take action in their own lives. This has led to an extraordinary explosion in the coverage of eco-issues in the media, which has made the work of those of us urgently trying to get people to take action far easier.

For example, the *Independent* now frequently devotes its entire front page to an environmental issue, something that would almost never have happened a few years ago. Even more importantly, one of the world's most powerful media tycoons, Rupert Murdoch, is now on record as saying that he believes human-caused carbon dioxide emissions are contributing to rising global temperatures. Indeed, his satellite TV station in Britain, BSkyB, which is led by his son James Murdoch, recently devoted an entire week to environmental issues on Sky News with a series entitled *Green Britain*. BSkyB has also become Britain's first carbon-neutral television station by offsetting all of their carbon dioxide emissions. Thus someone who up until very recently might have been seen as a corporate climate sceptic, and therefore an obstacle to be overcome, has in a very short space of time apparently become an ally.

John Howard, Prime Minister of Australia, has similarly abandoned the diminishing band of nay-sayers. Up until recently, Australia was one of George Bush's key international supporters in opposing the modest steps laid down by the Kyoto treaty to tackle the climate crisis. The background to this was that Australia relies very heavily on coal-powered electricity generation, which is the source of the highest emissions of carbon dioxide. However, a devastating prolonged drought, which was one of the predicted early consequences of the climate crisis in Australia, has forced environmental protection to the top of the political agenda. The Australian government has now abandoned its sceptical stance and in March 2007 demonstrated its new-found conviction by becoming the first developed nation to announce a ban on the old-fashioned wasteful tungsten light bulb. (The first ever country to do so was Cuba in 2005.)

In the UK even the supermarkets have been stirred into action by consumer pressure, with the encouraging spectacle of all the major players engaging in cut-throat competition to win the accolade of most eco-friendly supermarket. New announcements about how much of their packaging they are going to eliminate, how much of their carbon dioxide emissions they are going to cut and how much of their own waste they are going to recycle are made almost weekly. Even the US bogeyman Wal-Mart has declared its wish to be a 'good steward for the environment', with the ultimate target of using only renewable energy sources and producing zero waste.

All of this means that when you start to eco-audit your home or workplace, you will often find that there is already a huge groundswell of support among family members, partners and work colleagues that is just waiting for direction. Whereas a few years ago you might have met with significant opposition or even derision of your efforts, now it is more likely than not that your ideas will be greeted with enthusiasm and help. My recent experiences suggest that eco-auditing is like lighting a fire: once you start it, it spreads like wildfire. People take the approach into different areas of their lives and spread it way beyond the particular home or workplace where they started, which is one reason why eco-auditing is such a fun and easy way of spreading the eco-revolution.

Why the workplace?

There are a number of popular books that show people how to be more eco-friendly at home, including my own *Saving the Planet Without Costing the Earth*. Much of the information they give is now part of the mainstream. But not enough emphasis has yet been placed on how we can do the same at work, whatever our job. The fact is that many of us spend almost as many waking hours at our workplace as we do in our own homes. We therefore consume easily as much heat, light, water and food, and produce as much waste there, if not significantly more. So if we eco-audit only our home and not our workplace, we could be overlooking a large proportion of the environmental damage that our lifestyle is causing. Encouragingly, as this book demonstrates, there are lots of easy steps you can take, whatever your position at work, to make things more eco-friendly.

Whether you are a boss or an employee, if you want to persuade your colleagues and employers that they should have an eco-audit, it is useful to be equipped with good reasons why.

• It can help retain current customers: recent research in the UK found that over 82 per cent of consumers want to deal with a company that is eco-friendly.

• It can boost staff morale: many employees want to be as eco-friendly at work as they already are at home and can feel frustrated if their company does not enable them to be so.

• It can attract the best university graduates: a leading accountancy firm's research found that of the most highly qualified graduates, significant numbers wanted to work for environmentally responsible organizations.

• It can boost a company's positive public image.

• It can cut costs on heating, lighting, paper, etc.: a major employment agency recently had its IT department switch all its printers to automatic double-sided and saved over ten million sheets of paper per year.

• It can be fun for staff to learn new ways of doing traditional tasks.

• It can benefit staff if they take what they learn from a work eco-audit into their home.

• It can attract new customers.

• It can help to ensure a company's survival: as market and government regulations increasingly require companies to be eco-friendly, the development of new services and/or products to replace traditional ones that are damaging environmentally is vital.

• It will mean that the company's environmental ethics are part of the answer to the terrible environmental crisis that we now face.

In other words, not only is this ethically the right thing for companies to do but it will also ensure that employees and owners can feel good knowing they are part of the solution to the current climate crisis, not part of the problem.

Leading by example

One of the main foundations of my environmental work is Mahatma Gandhi's exhortation to 'be the change you want to see in the world'. As you will see in Chapter 11, I constantly seek to make my house as eco-friendly as possible, within the constraints of the time and money I have to hand. I find my progress in achieving a low carbon, waste and water lifestyle gives me the self-confidence to keep spreading the word to others. The energy carbon footprint for my home is less than zero and my mains water use is about one-fifth of the London average. Rather than producing bin-loads of rubbish, I produce just over half a wheelie bin of non-recycled domestic rubbish a *year*. And this year I actually became a net importer of waste, as I used about 32 wheelie bins of waste timber from my neighbourhood to fuel my new wood-burner. It gives me greater credibility when I carry out eco-audits, speak to groups on how to make their lives eco-friendly and carry out media interviews. There is nothing more undermining to a cause than its advocates doing the opposite of what they preach. We do not have to be perfect, but we really need to be doing our level best.

As you carry out your home or workplace eco-audit, it is equally important to remember the danger of slipping into self-righteousness or frustration at others' unwillingness to change their not so eco-friendly habits. A quiet eco-makeover of your own environmentally destructive habits will be far more powerful than any strident bullying of others. Another of Gandhi's themes, *ahimsa* or non-aggression, may also help. Gandhi felt it was of the highest importance not to wish ill on those who oppose or disagree with you. Respect people who do not wish at this moment to change or who believe that what you are proposing is not valid. Wasting energy on conflict and frustration, as I so often did, only saps your energy and is not very effective. The more you accept other people's right to a different viewpoint but continue gently with your own work, teaching people how to take positive action, the more you will find that it is enjoyable and rewarding. Combining these two approaches will help you to become a more successful eco-auditor and also a happier one!

Finally

Saving our planet, with its struggling natural biodiversity and failing ecological maintenance systems, may seem an insuperable task. It is the first global battle with no armed enemy to fight against. But while the threat is undoubtedly enormous, the positive aspect is its amazing potential to unite us all. Whatever our race, class, sexuality, age or religion, we have a common vested interest in ensuring that our lifestyles do not create havoc for the natural support systems of the planet. As an eco-auditor, I have worked with people and institutions from all the main religions and from none, with rich and poor, and with people of all races. It is a wonderful feeling to share their enthusiasm and the sense that together we can really make a difference. Leading by example, and by introducing the concept of eco-auditing into your home and your workplace, you too will become part of this positive, gentle eco-revolution. So get started!

Chapter 1

Why eco-auditing matters

A beginner's guide to global warming

Many members of your household and your work colleagues will be concerned by global warming. They will want to know what it actually means and what they can do to lessen the damage being caused. You will need to be equipped with knowledge of the basics so you can handle the questions that will be thrown at you in an eco-audit.

The air that we breathe and thus the atmosphere surrounding our planet is made up of invisible gases, such as oxygen, nitrogen, carbon dioxide, methane and water vapour. Without them there would be no life on earth. It was a fellow Irishman, John Tyndall, who discovered in the 1860s that heat can pass unhindered through some of these gases, such as oxygen and nitrogen, but that other gases, such as carbon dioxide, methane and water vapour, will block some heat trying to pass through them. Tyndall's discovery followed on from his creation of the world's first spectrophotometer, which is a fancy word for a machine that tests the heat-permeability of gases.

Tyndall realized that these gases controlled the earth's climate and that if they did not exist, then all the heat received from the sun during daylight hours would be very quickly lost after nightfall, resulting in vast areas of the planet experiencing freezing conditions at night all the year round. In other words, the heat-retaining properties of these gases make our planet habitable; it has since been calculated that the gases keep surface temperatures up to 30°C warmer. This benign effect is what has come to be called the 'greenhouse effect'.

In the late 1890s a Swedish scientist called Svante Arrhenius suggested that the burning of fossil fuels could lead to a build-up of carbon dioxide in the atmosphere, causing more heat to be retained and thus leading to an increase in the earth's surface temperatures.

Animals breathe in oxygen from the atmosphere and release carbon dioxide. Plants, on the other hand, take in carbon dioxide and release oxygen. The plants use this carbon dioxide in combination with other nutrients to create leaves, stems, flowers, fruit and wood. This continuous cycle of carbon storage and release by plants and animals is part of nature. When plants die and get buried in the soil, under certain conditions over millions of years they become fossil fuels. Fossil fuels include oil, natural gas, coal and lignite. When burned in the presence of oxygen, they release the carbon dioxide that has been stored over millions of years.

However, a problem occurs when massive amounts of carbon dioxide stored in fossil fuels are suddenly released over a short period of time. This is exactly what we started to do in the Industrial Revolution, which began in England in the middle of the 18th century and led to the burning of coal on a massive scale. With the spread of industrialization across the globe in the following centuries, the burning of fossil fuels increased exponentially. In 2006 worldwide emissions reached nearly 25 billion tonnes per year. We are now burning almost a million years' worth of fossil fuels every year! As the economies of many developing countries, such as India, China and Brazil, expand rapidly, emissions look set to rise for the foreseeable future unless drastic action is taken.

In a study published in June 2007, the United Nations Environment Programme (UNEP) reported that global carbon dioxide emissions from the burning of fossil fuels were increasing at a rate three times faster than in the 1990s. In other words, instead of increasing at 1 per cent per year, they were now increasing at over 3 per cent per year – precisely the wrong direction we should be going in order to avoid calamity.

The consequences of burning fossil fuels

When Arrhenius suggested that the burning of fossil fuels would raise global levels of carbon dioxide, he thought this would result in a modest benign warming. No one realized at that stage what the repercussions for climate and weather would be. Indeed, it was only in the late 1950s that an American scientist, David Keeling, started monitoring carbon dioxide levels in the atmosphere on an annual basis. He soon found that they were actually rising year on year.

Finally, in 1979, the first World Climate Conference alerted the public to the threat posed by rising levels of greenhouse gases. In 1988 the World Meteorological Organization set up the Intergovernmental Panel on Climate Change (IPCC) to ascertain the facts behind the alleged dangers of excessive emissions of greenhouse gases. The IPCC brought together scientific expertise from across the planet and has since then, at about five-yearly intervals, issued formal assessments of the information available to date. Each of their reports confirms that what Tyndall and Arrhenius predicted is actually happening, and at an unprecedented speed and scale.

The latest IPCC report, issued in 2007, is the most alarming to date. It was put together by over 2,000 scientists from countries across the globe, including the United States and oil-producing nations. Among their findings are:

• From 1850 to the present, 11 of the 12 warmest years have been since 1995.

• Levels of CO_2 in the atmosphere are higher than at any time over the last 650,000 years.

• Global warming is expected to be 3°C by 2100.

• If greenhouse gases are not curbed temperatures may rise by over 6°C by 2100.

• Atmospheric concentrations of water vapour are 4 per cent higher than in 1970 because of evaporation from the world's oceans as a result of warming.

• Sea levels will rise significantly even if emission levels are stabilized.

• Hurricanes are likely to be stronger, with increased rainfall.

• The Arctic Ocean is likely to be completely ice-free in summer.

• Heat waves are expected to be more intense, longer-lasting and more frequent.

• There is over 90 per cent certainty that human actions are responsible for global warming.

The consequences of climate change

At the beginning of your eco-audit, people at home or at work might well ask you what exactly the threat from climate chaos is and what various predictions of rising global temperatures mean in reality. Some people genuinely imagine that global warming could be pleasant, especially if they live in cold, wet climates! The following points will help you to answer these questions. Remember as you read them that the EU is considered radical for proposing policies aimed at preventing a rise of more than 2°C.

Desertification
The range of the world's existing deserts will radically expand and redesertification stretching from Montana to Texas is threatened if temperatures rise above 2.5°C. Desertification of southern Europe would take place if temperature rises reached 4.5°C.

Rising sea levels
Water expands as it gets warmer and most of the rise in sea levels over the past century is due to the already existing rise in ocean

temperatures. However, if temperatures rise over 2.5°C, then the huge land-based glaciers in Greenland and Antarctica will start to melt irreversibly. Should they melt completely, sea levels would be a staggering 70 metres higher than in 2007.

Melting glaciers

The annual melting in spring and summer of mountain glaciers in South America, Europe and, most importantly, Asia supplies fresh water to literally hundreds of millions of people. All of the Andean glaciers are expected to be gone by 2050.

Chinese scientists predict that all of the Himalayan glaciers will be gone by 2100. UNEP states that 40 per cent of the world's population depends on Himalayan meltwater for irrigation and drinking water.

Collapse in food production

Chaotic weather conditions will play havoc with crops. It is feared that cereal crop yields will drop by up to 20 per cent by 2050.

Destruction of forests

The Amazon rainforest would turn into desert if temperatures reached 3.5°C. No forests anywhere on the planet would survive a global rise in temperatures of 6°C.

Intensification of hurricanes and storms

Scientists state that the strength of hurricanes is proportional to the amount of heat stored in the ocean surfaces. Thus the warmer the oceans, the more powerful the hurricanes will be. Should global warming run out of control and reach 6°C, then the world would be lashed by super-hurricanes and typhoons, bringing devastation wherever they hit.

Elimination of animal and plant species

The 2006 Stern Review found that a 2°C rise in temperatures would result in the extinction of up to 30 per cent of all known species. Almost nothing would survive a sustained 6°C rise.

Acidification of oceans

The oceans absorb carbon dioxide from the atmosphere as part of the planet's natural stabilizing mechanism. However, if they absorb too much carbon dioxide the oceans will become so acidic that almost nothing will be able to live in them.

Disastrous heat waves

Extreme heat events will occur more frequently, with temperatures exceeding 50°C in many parts of the world.

Spread of tropical diseases

As temperatures rise, many tropical diseases such as malaria will spread, leading to the deaths of millions of people. The increased occurrence of tick-borne Lyme disease and encephalitis in northern Europe is already partially attributed to climate change.

Is climate change already an urgent problem?

Many political leaders around the world now acknowledge that climate change is the most serious long-term threat to our way of life, but the problem is that it is already happening. To galvanize your family or work colleagues into taking action now, you will need to be able to give them examples of the already existing effects of rising temperatures.

Facts about existing global warming

- **Desertification** The Gobi Desert is expanding at a rate of 10,360 square kilometres per year, forcing people across three Chinese provinces to abandon their homes, while in Nigeria over 3,370 square kilometres are turning to desert every year.

- **Rising sea levels** Global sea levels are already rising, with average increases of 2 mm per year between 1961 and 2003 and of more than 3 mm between 1993 and 2003. The Tuvalu group of islands is already having to be evacuated, with 3,000 people forced out by sea flooding.

- **Melting glaciers** A third of Peru's glaciers have already gone and the Chinese Academy of Sciences has reported that the Himalayan glaciers are shrinking by 7 per cent per year.

- **Collapse in food production** US scientists found that rising temperatures caused a global reduction in cereal crops of up to 44 million tonnes per year between 1981 and 2002.

- **Destruction of forests** Termites, which flourish in warmer temperatures, are devastating large tracts of Alaskan forests as Arctic temperatures rise at a faster rate than the rest of the planet. In the UK chestnut trees are dying because warmer winters mean the destructive weevil that lives on the tree is no longer held in check by frost.

- **Intensification of hurricanes** Scientists calculate that the number of category 4 and 5 hurricanes has nearly doubled since 1970. The largest number of hurricanes in a single year was recorded in 2005.

■ **Loss of life and creation of refugees** The UN estimates that 160,000 people a year are already dying from the consequences of climate change and that there are over 25 million environmental refugees already displaced from their homes.

■ **Disappearing sea ice** Total Arctic sea ice has been shrinking by 2.7 per cent every decade since 1978 and summer ice has been shrinking even faster. The Northeast Passage was navigable for the first time in history in September 2007. In addition, a terrifying 22.5 per cent of the Arctic summer sea ice disappeared in 2007, following the previous record of 12.5 per cent melt in 2005, raising fears that the tipping point for irreversible melting of the Arctic summer sea ice may have passed.

■ **Global temperatures** The average temperature of the planet increased by 0.6°C in the 20th century.

■ **Spread of tropical diseases** Malaria has already spread into the high-altitude areas of Kenya, where it was almost unheard of 30 years ago.

What can we do about climate change?

There is no doubt that the biggest issue for most people who decide to undertake an eco-audit is reducing their damaging contributions to climate change. Jargon phrases such as 'low-carbon economy', 'zero-carbon homes', 'carbon offsetting', 'carbon-neutral businesses', 'carbon footprint', 'carbon dioxide equivalents', 'tipping points' and 'contraction and convergence' are constantly bandied about these days and it is important to know what they mean.

Low-carbon economy

The first thing to understand is the link between the emission of carbon dioxide into the atmosphere and day-to-day life at home and at work. The simple fact is that the production of almost anything we now consume involves the use of fossil fuels. Industry uses oil, coal, gas and electricity to power its machinery. Cars, planes, trucks and ships use oil-based products to power their engines. The electricity industry uses coal, oil and gas to power its turbines. Homes and businesses use gas, oil and coal to heat their premises and provide hot water. Even the plastic used in the packaging industry is actually made from oil.

Thus a low-carbon economy would be one that seeks to reduce radically the use of fossil fuels. This can be done in two ways: by finding alternative sources of energy, such as wind and solar power, which do not emit carbon dioxide; and by eliminating wasteful and unnecessary consumption of energy and resources. Ideally, you want to have the same quality of life using vastly less resources.

Zero-carbon homes and businesses

Zero-carbon premises are ones that use no fossil fuels to power heating or lighting. If there is any electricity, it will come from renewable sources, such as wind, solar electric panels or micro-hydro generators. Similarly, hot water will be provided by renewables, such as wood, solar hot-water panels or electricity powered by green energy. To have all the space heating provided by renewables usually requires biomass or super-insulation and extensive passive solar heating to be incorporated into the design. The most common form of zero-carbon space heating is wood-burning. (We will go into these technologies and terminologies in greater depth in Chapter 8.)

Carbon offsetting

Carbon offsetting is the practice of compensating for the carbon dioxide emissions released from your home or business by funding the reduction of carbon dioxide emissions elsewhere. A number of charities and businesses now offer this service and in general they take three approaches. The first is to plant trees; the second is to fund energy-efficiency measures in poor countries; and the third is to pay for renewable energy systems in developing countries.

A mature tree absorbs and stores throughout its lifetime up to a tonne of carbon dioxide. Carbon-offsetting companies state that funding the planting of trees will thus partially compensate for the carbon dioxide released by your plane journey, heating or lighting, etc. The installation of energy-saving light bulbs in South African schools will save over a quarter of a tonne of carbon dioxide per 20-watt energy-saving bulb during its lifetime if it is replacing a 100-watt tungsten bulb.

Your family or work colleagues might have heard arguments against carbon offsetting. The three arguments I come across most often are that the carbon dioxide stored in trees will be released if the tree dies; that certain carbon-offsetting companies are dubious; and that carbon offsetting is just a way for rich people to avoid looking at how they can reduce their carbon dioxide emissions in the first place. While there is some truth in these arguments, the fact remains that well-run carbon-offsetting schemes have a positive role to play in moving us towards a low-carbon economy.

Reasons to carbon offset

- Unlike most so-called environmental taxes levied by the government, which disappear in general taxation, this voluntary tax on carbon emissions is used specifically for environmental purposes.

- The polluter pays for the pollution caused, which is a long-term campaign aim of environmentalists.

- Paying for the replanting of lost woodlands helps to restore vital wildlife habitats.

- Paying for your pollution brings home the message that carbon emissions are destructive and need to be dealt with.

- Paying for renewable energy projects in the developing world means that people there can have a better quality of life without emitting destructive CO_2.

- Paying for energy-efficiency measures for poor people means that they save money on bills and emit less CO_2.

- Research has shown that the vast majority of those who offset carbon emissions from their home or company also seek to reduce their overall emissions.

- As governments are highly unlikely to ban planes, there will still be significant CO_2 emissions from flying over the coming years, so carbon offsetting will raise urgently needed money to help tackle climate change.

- The planting of trees does store CO_2 and even if one tree dies its wood can be used as a carbon neutral fuel and another can be planted in its place, especially if the money from carbon offsetting was used to purchase the land for tree planting.

- Many excellent schemes are endorsed by major environmental charities and independent standards are also being developed.

Carbon-neutral home or business

Carbon-neutral premises are ones that have dealt with all their carbon dioxide emissions by using combinations of renewable energy, energy efficiency and carbon offsetting. The main difference between carbon-neutral and zero-carbon premises is that the former still have emissions, all of which they carbon offset. While the ideal is to have zero-carbon premises, in truth this is very difficult to achieve for most existing urban buildings. Slashing the first 50 per cent of emissions is often quite easy, but the next 30 per cent is more challenging and achieving the final 20 per cent is very challenging in many circumstances. It is, of course, possible to have carbon-neutral premises by simply offsetting all the existing carbon dioxide emissions. Rightly, however, this is not regarded as best practice, since it means that no responsibility is being taken for wasted emissions. In fact, for some companies this approach seems to be a shortcut to easy eco-publicity.

While acknowledging this, it is still far better that a company undertakes to provide funding for positive action on emissions elsewhere than doing absolutely nothing. And in the meantime, rather than waiting for governments to take action, if we could persuade the majority of homes and companies to carbon offset their emissions through consumer, employee and management pressure, billions would be raised for work on emissions reduction that is urgently needed now.

Carbon footprint

An annual carbon footprint is the total amount of carbon dioxide emitted by a house, factory, company or individual over the previous year. Carbon dioxide emissions are usually given by weight, the standard being by metric tonne. However, you will find an amazing range of ways in which carbon footprints are measured, because there are almost as many approaches as there are research institutes. Some assess all the measurable fossil-fuel energy used by a premises or business. Others take into account the energy used by suppliers. Yet others use the weight of carbon in the carbon dioxide molecule rather than the total weight of the gas. Instead of getting involved in a whole host of complex calculations, I generally calculate the measurable carbon dioxide emissions, which I refer to as the annual energy carbon footprint: basically, this covers the emissions from heating, electricity, private transport and flights.

Carbon dioxide equivalents

Yet another approach is to estimate the carbon dioxide equivalent of all greenhouse gas emissions: the shorthand for this is CO_2e. We have already mentioned that there are gases in addition to carbon dioxide that contribute to the greenhouse effect, such as methane, nitrous oxide and water vapour. Scientists have developed a way of relating the contribution of these gases to global warming, comparing their effect with that of carbon dioxide over a period of time. The figure beside each gas in the table opposite represents the amount of times it is more powerful than carbon dioxide as a global warming agent over a century.

Methane is the main component of the natural gas burned in our homes and power stations. Among the principal sources of methane gas emissions into the atmosphere are farm animals and the fermentation of decaying plants and other organic materials, such as sewage and municipal waste, in anaerobic (air-free) conditions. The livestock sector in general (primarily cattle, chickens and pigs) produces 37 per cent of all human-related methane. In addition, vast quantities of methane are stored in the frozen crust of the earth in, for example, the permafrosts of Siberia and North America, while similarly large amounts of methane salts have formed at the bottom of the oceans over millions of years from the remains of sea plants and plankton.

Agriculture is the main source of nitrous oxide emissions, because nitrogen fertilizers cause bacteria to produce more nitrous oxide.

HFC-23 is generated as a waste gas in the manufacture of another hydrofluorocarbon, HFC-22, which is a gas used as a refrigerant and as a raw material for other products. HFCs are one of the greenhouse gases covered under the Kyoto Protocol.

Sulphur hexa-fluoride is used in the electrical industry as an insulator.

Comparing gases

Gas	CO_2e	Years in atmosphere
Carbon dioxide	1	50–200
Methane	21	12
Nitrous oxide	296	114
Hydrofluorocarbon (HFC-23)	12,000	260
Sulphur hexa-fluoride	22,200	3,200

Tipping points

The mention of methane may bring up the term 'tipping point' during your eco-audit and again you will need to know what this means. Over the last 100 years, as we have released more and more greenhouse gases into the atmosphere, the earth's temperature has gradually increased. Many scientists fear that if a certain point is passed, what they call 'feedback mechanisms' will kick in and the process will become irreversible. In that case, global warming would run out of control, leading to the end of life on the planet as we know it. Any number of problems could result in a tipping point being reached. One such, known as the 'albedo effect', concerns the possible repercussions of warming at the North and South Poles. The whiteness of the huge areas of ice and snow there reflects significant amounts of the sun's rays, preventing them from heating the planet and melting the surface cover. However, should the ice and snow begin to melt and shrink, because of temperature rises, the resulting cleared ocean in the Arctic and landmass in the Antarctic would absorb more heat, which would in turn melt more ice. The vicious circle thus started might not finish until all the ice and snow had melted, resulting in almost all the coastlines of the planet having to be redrawn. There is significant scientific evidence to suggest that this is already beginning to happen in the Arctic.

The methane that is at present stored in the frozen permafrost wastes of Siberia and North America is another potential tipping point. Permafrost is the term given to the deep, permanently frozen soils within the Arctic and Antarctic Circle. If it is released, it would cause runaway, uncontrollable global warming, as methane is 23 times more powerful than carbon dioxide as a global warming gas. Alarmingly, scientists from Siberia reported in 2006 that methane was beginning to escape from the warming permafrost. Similar reports that the permafrost is melting in North America have been coming for some time.

Water vapour is another potential tipping point for irreversible global warming. Like most of the other greenhouse gases, it occurs naturally and is essential for maintaining the planet's existing mainly benign temperatures. However, as global warming increases, so will the amount of water vapour evaporating from the world's oceans, and the more water vapour in the atmosphere, the more likely temperatures are to rise – another vicious circle in the making.

The most terrifying doomsday scenario concerns the methane salts deposited at the bottom of the oceans. Should these start to be released as temperatures on the ocean bed rise, scientists fear that the resulting fire storms could consume the organic life on the surface of the planet, in which case there would be no hope of our civilization surviving.

Contraction and convergence

Historically, most greenhouse gases are released by the rich developed countries, while developing countries have had low emissions. But in order to tackle poverty many of these poorer countries are now industrializing, with a consequent move towards Western levels of emissions. If the world's poorer southern nations continue in their push towards industrialized economies, this could result in carbon dioxide emissions increasing by over 500 per cent, guaranteeing a climatic Armageddon. The solution that has been proposed is a concept known as 'contraction and convergence', whereby the UN scientifically agrees the level at which carbon dioxide emissions must be capped if the climate crisis is not to run out of control. This amount is then divided among the world's population and each person on the planet is allocated a carbon dioxide allowance. These allowances can then be assigned to each country, depending on their population. Countries exceeding their allowance would have to buy permits to pollute from those that emit less than their allowance.

The beauty of this scheme is that it transfers investment capital to the world's poorest countries, the ones emitting tiny amounts of greenhouse gases, thus enabling their inhabitants to climb out of poverty. However, getting agreement from the polluting nations or those who are now rapidly developing, such as Brazil, India and China, is not going to be easy. Therefore, individuals need to start taking matters into their own hands and try to implement their own quotas. Total global emissions in 2006 were estimated to be 25 billion tonnes of carbon dioxide (and growing at 3.3 per cent per year). The global population is estimated at 6.6 billion people and is predicted to reach 9.5 billion by 2050. This gives current emissions per person of 3.75 tonnes of carbon dioxide annually. So the average UK citizen, who emits 9.5 tonnes of carbon dioxide per year, would need to cut their emissions by about 60 per cent to reach the current global average.

But some scientists believe that we need a cut of between 80 and 90 per cent by 2030 if we are to avoid dangerous runaway global overheating. This would mean an average allowance of about 0.5 tonnes per person at current population figures. My own view is that there is already too much CO_2 in the atmosphere and we should not only be seeking to cut human emissions to almost zero but also be seeking to reduce the overall tonnage in the atmosphere.

Average CO_2 emissions

- The average emissions per person in the UK in 2006 were 9.50 tonnes

- The average emissions per person in the world in 2006 were 3.75 tonnes

- The ideal maximum annual emissions per person should be 0.50 tonnes

Tonnes of CO_2 emissions per capita per year

Country	Tonnes of CO_2
USA	20
Australia	19
UK	9.5
China	3
India	1
Ghana	0.25
Bangladesh	0.25

Get carbon fit!

It will be obvious by now that no one should under-estimate the magnitude of the threats facing us. So, having made the case for urgent action and explained the various climate change jargon being used, it is now time to take the first practical step in your eco-audit. In order to draw up a plan for making your home and your workplace eco-friendly, you will need to calculate your energy carbon footprint. It is my intention that reducing one's footprint – and being proud of how carbon fit you are – will become the eco-equivalent of feeling good about a physically healthier lifestyle.

Many government agencies divide up national carbon footprints between the various job sectors, such as industry and transport, but this makes it difficult for individuals to take action to reduce their own footprints. As I have already mentioned, carbon footprints are calculated in many different ways but my preference is to stick to things such as heating, electricity, private transport and flights. These are easily measurable by people in their day-to-day lives, unlike the huge complexity of calculating the exact amount of carbon used in preparing a particular meal. This is not to say such issues are unimportant – indeed, as Chapter 10 shows, food is the source of up to a third of our carbon dioxide emissions – but they require detailed academic investigation due to the large amount of variables involved.

In carrying out home and business eco-audits, I come across an enormous range of annual energy carbon footprints among my domestic clients, from the highest, at 66 tonnes, for a well-off Hertfordshire family with a swimming pool, to the lowest, an astonishingly small 1.4 tonnes, for the entire family of the Friends of the Earth press officer, Neil Verlander. Average household emissions in the UK are 6.2 tonnes, according to the Department of the Environment.

When working with clients, I ask them to fill in a form listing how much electricity, gas, heating oil, coal, water, rubbish, petrol or diesel they have used, how many flights they have taken in the previous year and how many times a week they eat meat. You can fill in this form at home or at work too, using the eco-audit form on pages 272–75. Simple calculations then convert these figures into tonnes of carbon dioxide and an energy carbon footprint for the year. It is true, of course, that almost everything we do in life, from breathing (like all other animals, we breathe in oxygen and breathe out carbon dioxide) to shopping and eating and drinking, will result in carbon dioxide emissions because of the production, transport, packaging and disposal involved.

The essential message is that wasteful consumption leads to increased levels of carbon dioxide, which is leading to climate catastrophe. One way of getting this across is to calculate the amount of water you have used and the amount of unrecycled rubbish you have dumped in the previous year. The results could stagger you.

Depressingly, following publication of the Stern Review on the economic implications of climate change, which so graphically set out the threats posed, the UK government agreed to spend:
• £65 billion on developing and maintaining nuclear weapons between now and 2050;
• £23 billion on building new schools;
• £10 billion on building, equipping and running two new aircraft carriers;
• and just £1 million extra on installing a tiny number of renewable energy systems, such as solar panels, in UK homes over the following six months.

Electricity

Electricity production is responsible for 40 per cent of carbon emissions worldwide due to the burning of fossil fuels such as coal, oil and gas in power stations. To find out your electricity carbon footprint, look at your electricity bills for the last year to see how many kilowatt-hours (kWh) you used. Simply subtract the reading for the start of the year from the reading at the end of the year, then multiply the result by a conversion ratio of 0.43 to get your footprint in kg of CO_2. Another way to do this is to take readings directly from your electricity meter at the start and end of the year.

For example, if you used the average UK household 5,200 kWh, the calculation would be as follows:

5,200 kWh x 0.43 = 2,236 kg = 2.2 tonnes CO_2.

Note The conversion ratio will vary from year to year as the mix of fuels varies. Thus if the government allows a move towards more coal, as has been the case in recent years, then the amount of carbon dioxide per kWh of electricity will increase. The National Energy Foundation website usually provides an up-to-date figure on their carbon calculator.

Gas, oil and coal

Gas and oil emit far less carbon dioxide per kWh than fossil-fuel-sourced electricity, but because they heat your home and water, both of which take large amounts of energy, they usually contribute more to your carbon debt.

To calculate your domestic gas carbon footprint, again look at last year's bills and see how many kWh of gas you used. You then multiply this figure by a conversion ratio of 0.19. Alternatively, as with electricity, you could use your gas meter readings. For example, if you used the average UK household 33,500 kWh, the calculation would be as follows:

33,500 kWh x 0.19 = 6,365 kg = 6.4 tonnes CO_2.

For oil and coal the conversion ratios are different. To calculate your domestic oil carbon footprint, multiply the number of litres of oil you used by 2.68. For example, if you used the average UK household 2,000 litres of oil, then the calculation would be:

2,000 x 2.68 = 5,360 kg = 5.4 tonnes CO_2.

For your domestic coal carbon footprint, multiply the number of tonnes of coal you used by 2.42. For example, if you used the average UK household 2.5 tonnes of coal, the calculation would be:

2.5 x 2.42 = 6.05 tonnes CO_2.

Car use

Surface transport contributes over 20 per cent to carbon dioxide emissions in the UK, much of it from private car use. To calculate your carbon dioxide emissions by distance driven, the calculation is as follows: multiply distance driven per year in kilometres by 0.23 or multiply distance driven in miles by 0.36. For example, the average UK motorist drives 13,920 kilometres (8,700 miles) per year, and the calculation is as follows:

13,920 kilometres x 0.23 = 3,201 = 3.2 tonnes CO_2.

If you want to make your calculation based on litres of petrol used instead, the conversion ratio is 2.68.

Flights

A lot of attention is currently being paid to carbon emissions from flights, even though they make up only 2 per cent of total UK emissions. Their effect is further amplified due to the fact that the emissions are released high in the atmosphere. However, this obscures the fact that for the rich, flights contribute a huge amount to their carbon debt. A flight from the UK to New York will add 1.2 tonnes, to Japan 2 tonnes and to New Zealand a whopping 4.2 tonnes. To put things into perspective, this is exactly three times what the entire four-member Verlander family emits for all energy use in an entire year. With budget airlines causing an explosion in air travel and the EU and US governments agreeing an open-skies treaty, emissions are expected to double in the next 30 years, requiring even more dramatic cuts in other emissions if we are to avoid irreversible climate disaster.

The CarbonNeutral Company website will provide data on carbon dioxide emissions between almost every airport worldwide, while the National Energy Foundation website will convert miles flown, if known, into tonnes of carbon dioxide.

Unfortunately, some of my clients still use private jets, which requires a different calculation!

Non-direct energy emissions

The fact that you are now in a position to measure your direct energy carbon footprint does not mean that other sources of emissions can be ignored. For example, the UK emits 4 million tonnes of carbon dioxide in pumping water around the country every year. The average personal daily water usage in London is 160 litres. Similarly, meat consumption has a massive carbon footprint, with methane and other emissions from cows and other livestock contributing over 18 per cent to global emissions.

Calculating your energy carbon footprint is the first step in any carbon fitness regime. It is the equivalent of weighing yourself when you join the gym. Ignore the nay-sayers who fear change, shouting that there is no point getting fit because the Americans or the Australians are fatter, or that carbon-emaciated Indians also consume carbon. It is true that the USA contributes over 21 per cent of global emissions, but just because they are carbon wasteful is no reason for us not to lead by example, getting carbon-fit ourselves. The fact that the average Indian emits less than a eighth of the carbon dioxide of the average Briton puts even greater moral pressure on us in the rich developed world to set our house in order first, if we are to avoid the catastrophe that Sir Nicholas Stern has warned is careering down the tracks towards us.

So, get those gas and electricity bills out and do the simple calculations on the eco-audit form on pages 272–75 for your household or business.

Chapter 2

The basics of eco-auditing

Where do you start?

This chapter covers in broad outline the practical steps you will need to take to approach an eco-audit at home or at work. Detailed information about specific aspects of your premises' environmental performance will be dealt with in succeeding chapters. But before we start on the actual nitty-gritty of the eco-audit, it is worth pausing to consider various personal and psychological issues that may arise once you start this process and to consider approaches that will help you to deal with them.

It is crucial to remember when carrying out an eco-audit of a home or business that, unless you live or work by yourself, the process involves fellow human beings and will more than likely challenge aspects of their current behaviour and habits with which they are familiar and happy. The fundamental starting point must be respect for others and their different attitudes. Mahatma Gandhi would have phrased it in terms of *ahimsa* or non-aggression. It is important to approach people at home or at work from a constructive point of view, no matter how urgent the issues or how passionate you feel about them.

One of the easiest ways to understand this is to think how you feel when other people, be it your partner, kids, parents, work colleagues or your boss, try to force you to change your way of thinking or doing things to fit in with them. You know that hectoring or disparagement will more often than not only get your back up and make you close your mind to change. Rather than thinking of the eco-audit as a severe inspection, the key is to see it as a gentle but valuable service, the importance of which is up to the receiver to appreciate – or not. In a free world, that is absolutely their prerogative.

If you want to be a relaxed but effective eco-auditor and avoid getting frustrated when someone resists what appears to you to be a perfectly reasonable suggestion about improving their environmental performance, it is important to understand that there are psychological issues involved when asking others to change. I spent many years being angered by the failure of colleagues or those I saw as opponents in my early campaigning and political days to understand the urgency of taking action to deal with environmental threats. It was only once I came across the psychological theories that relate to human beings' healthy need for stability, which makes change seem threatening, that I started to find a greater calmness in how I went about my campaigning work and latterly my eco-auditing.

The 70:25:5 approach to change

Basically we need to feel there is a solid foundation to our lives if we are to function in a healthy manner. In other words, if our lives change 100 per cent every day, then we would end up with no job, no partner, no food, no home, no money – in the end we would simply die. It is almost totally impossible to survive with continuous total change in our lives. Researchers found that, roughly speaking, the ideal balance is 70 per cent stability, 25 per cent open to gradual change and 5 per cent open to radical and urgent change.

The example that I often use to demonstrate this is a relationship. If you are in a happy relationship, you want it to remain stable. But if the relationship is 100 per cent the same every day, there is a very high risk that one or both of you will get thoroughly bored and the relationship will hit the rocks. So it is important to make room for growth and development, which is what the 25 per cent represents. However, should your happy relationship suddenly become abusive or violent for whatever reason, you would need to do something about it immediately. In this particular example, that might mean seeking professional help – say, seeing a counsellor or, if really necessary for your own protection, a divorce lawyer. In other words, you would need to access the 5 per cent area open to radical change.

The same concept can be applied to families, companies, local councils and governments in varying degrees. If a business or organization were to change 100 per cent every day it would soon go out of business, as its customers and staff lost track of its purpose. Local government often comes under fire for not being open to radical change, but it is essential for the safety and survival of the community that its organizational and political structures rest on secure and stable foundations. It is therefore usually essential that such structures change in a gradual and thoughtful manner, only when the case for change is well proven.

When you approach an eco-audit, it is important to remember that what you are actually asking people to consider is moving out of their 70 per cent stability and security zone. These same people also know, either consciously or subconsciously, that stability is crucial to their future survival. However, leaving the security of your comfort zone does not necessarily mean you are risking danger. Indeed, it can often mean nothing more than simply changing an environmentally destructive habit for a benign new one, such as turning off your office lights at lunchtime.

Four years ago, when I was writing my first book, I thought that we had until about 2050 to complete the changeover from a consumer society to a low-carbon (i.e. low or no fossil fuel) economy. Since society currently changes fairly comprehensively on a roughly 100-year cycle, this did not seem too radical or revolutionary. I felt that by demonstrating the simple steps I had taken in my own life, I could encourage others to start the process of making their own lives more eco-friendly. In other words, without knowing it, I was gently encouraging them to move slowly from the stability zone into the 25 per cent zone, where they would be open to gradual change.

However, in light of all the alarming scientific reports on climate chaos, accelerating emissions of carbon dioxide and information about potential tipping points that could lead to irreversible climate change, I have been forced reluctantly to abandon that cosy approach. I recently attended a summit in London of the UK's leading environmentalists at which a number of senior people expressed the view that we should not reveal the urgency of the situation, as it could lead the public to panic or abandon efforts to reduce carbon emissions because it was too late. I disagreed strongly, believing that responsibly conveyed truth is always the best public policy.

It is now incumbent upon those of us who are aware of the depth of the crisis to understand that what we now need to do is enable people to move from their 70 per cent stability zone, through the 25 per cent gradual-change zone, to the 5 per cent radical-change zone as fast as possible. The challenge, therefore, is how to do this in such a way that people will feel safe and confident. In my view, that means demonstrating by personal example how to have an eco-friendly lifestyle and educating by eco-audit how to effect the necessary changes at home and at work. Politics and campaigning are important too, of course, but the gentle eco-revolution will only start from the bottom up. While recognizing the extreme urgency of the situation, it will help reduce your stress levels if you remember that those who oppose your viewpoint are more often than not just articulating that normally healthy defence of society's current status quo. In the challenge to get across your message in such a way that people will feel safe about changing their lifestyle, eco-auditing will be one of the most effective tools at your disposal.

Grief at sudden endings

Another psychological insight that will help you to understand what is going on when you are eco-auditing concerns conscious and subconscious responses to death or sudden endings. There is no doubt that the oil- and fossil-fuel-based economy and the wasteful, consumerist society that developed in the 20th century have to be brought to an end if we are to avoid the worst effects of the climate crisis. Millions of people already know this, to a greater or lesser extent, and will often go through a process of bereavement in relation to the death of this type of economy and lifestyle just as an individual does when someone close to them dies. In her seminal book *On Death and Dying*, Elisabeth Kübler-Ross identified the 'five stages of grief' that a patient experiences when informed of a terminal prognosis. To demonstrate the parallels, I have adapted her five stages to apply to the current climate situation.

Denial (this isn't happening to me)

The denial of fundamental scientific facts was the line adopted by George Bush, the oil-industry-sponsored Global Climate Coalition and millions of people across the world. In many ways, this is a perfectly natural response for organizations and people whose incomes or lifestyles depended on the burning of fossil fuels. However, denial is for many now coming to an end. Even companies like DuPont, Shell, BP, DaimlerChrysler and General Motors have abandoned the anti-climate-crisis coalitions and stopped funding the global climate-crisis-denial campaigns. Similarly millions of people around the world are no longer arguing against the facts but are asking instead what they can do to lessen the problem. In the last two years, in the vast majority of organizations that I visit, I find nearly all of the staff are now very supportive of actions to reduce their organization's environmental impact, even if the extreme urgency required has not yet hit home for most people.

Anger (why is this happening to me?)

This part of the response, often directed blindly against all 'environmentalists', often takes the form of name-calling – 'eco-fascists', 'eco-nutters', etc. Instead of dealing constructively with the death of their previously comfortable, fossil-fuel-powered, consumerist lifestyles, people sometimes find it easier to hit out at the messenger. So it is important as an eco-auditor or environ-mentalist not to take any anger personally but to see it as a very occasional natural part of the process by which individuals and organizations come to terms with perceived or actual loss.

Bargaining (I promise I'll be a better person if...)

This is something you will hear from people and organizations. For example, BP has recently announced that it will be reducing carbon emissions from its petrol stations. This in itself is very laudable, but such emissions are in fact only a tiny fraction of the overall emissions released from BP's global oil and fossil-fuel business worldwide every year. Such an approach reminds me of the prayer attributed to St Augustine: 'Help me to stop being a sinner, but not yet!'

For an eco-auditor, it is often important to support such moves rather than rejecting them outright as hypocritical. BP and some of the other major oil companies have moved beyond denial of global warming or angry attacks on environmentalists, but this is just the start. If you recognize that it is part of the process of coming to terms with the death of the oil economy, then you can more calmly help them move on to the next stage. The same is true with individuals: you must be positive about what they are already doing if you want to be effective in helping them move to a more radical limitation of their environmentally damaging actions.

Depression (I don't care any more)

The most common expression of this emotion I hear in relation to the climate crisis is that if America, China and India, the commercial competition or the neighbours, are not doing anything about it, why should we? Then there is the viewpoint that as the climate is already so seriously damaged, it is too late to do anything and we might as well continue with our environmentally damaging habits as before. I find it mildly amusing that people at this stage of grief can switch from using the wealthy of America as an excuse for doing nothing to blaming some of the poorest in the world (in China and India).

The fact is that while America does produce almost 25 per cent of the world's carbon dioxide emissions, 75 per cent (i.e. the vast majority) is produced by the rest of the world. So if those of us not in America take action, we can really make a significant difference. It would also make a difference inside America, not only because the emerging eco-technologies would become cheaper from our mass adoption and so more readily implemented, but also because it would bolster politically the large body of opinion there that is already calling for urgent action on the issue across the United States.

As regards the developing countries, there is no doubt that their rapid industrialization and economic expansion are leading to an enormous increase in greenhouse gases. However, it is important to remember that their per capita emissions and individual wealth are tiny compared with those of people living in Western developed nations, such as the UK and Australia (see page 41). You must persuade people during your eco-audit that they have a responsibility to try first to reduce their emissions to the global average of 3.75 tonnes and then to get them down to an average of less than 1 tonne per year if the planet is to have any hope of avoiding the worst effects of the climate crisis. There is absolutely no denying that this is a huge challenge for Western oil-guzzling consumers, but in this case there is no alternative.

In relation to the argument that if the neighbours are not doing anything, there is no point taking action, the most powerful response is to say that the world only ever changes when individuals change their lives first, thus showing what can be done. In other words, only by individuals showing that radical changes can work will the rest of society feel safe to follow.

Acceptance (I'm ready for whatever comes)

This is when you know that the only part of your job now left is to give the person or organization the practical tools they need to take positive action and actually change to a low-carbon, non-consumerist lifestyle or style of organizational management.

The home or workplace where you are carrying out your eco-audit may be at any of the above stages, but your task is always to gently move them on towards 'acceptance'.

Finally, something I agree with George Bush about. He refers to our oil consumption as an addiction. This is a very useful metaphor. Our dependency started in the late 19th century and became more and more damaging as the 20th century progressed. However, like all destructive addictions, it can be treated!

How to approach initiating an eco-audit

If you have chosen to carry out an eco-audit of where you live or work, rather than being professionally commissioned or acting as an outside volunteer, your position in the premises will determine how you set about your task. The main thing to remember is that you want family and work colleagues on your side rather than getting their backs up.

At home your approach will depend on whether you are a single person, in a relationship, a parent, a teenager or a child. If you are in a relationship, you should involve your partner, just as you would with any other decision that affects both of your lives. With the right approach, an eco-audit can be fun and even enrich your relationship if you are both able to savour the satisfaction of seeing your environmental performance improve year on year. However, like anything else in relationships, if approached in the wrong way it can be destructive. The huge increase in concern about environmental issues among the wider public over the last few years has, not surprisingly, begun to put strain on some relationships, as one partner realizes the need for urgent action while the other does not. As with any other relationship difference, this will need to be handled sensitively. I think the best approach is to make as much of your own behaviour as eco-friendly as possible, while respecting your partner and discussing with them what they are willing to do jointly. In the end, you have to let them get on with how they want to live, difficult as that may be. However, having lived alone for some time, I confess that I would find it challenging to be with someone who did not have an eco-friendly lifestyle!

If you are carrying out an eco-audit for a couple's house or a business partnership, you will sometimes find that one person is really enthusiastic about making changes to their lifestyle but the other is not. In other words, you are caught in the middle of what is a normal relationship tussle, with one partner wanting you to endorse unreservedly their deep green eco-proposals, while the other wants you to rubbish them as unrealistic. My general approach is to try not to take sides but rather to see if there are any win/win solutions, with a green approach the reluctant partner may find acceptable. For example, if someone is horrified at the idea of an entire roof on their traditional rustic family home being devoted to a large solar electric array, they may find having a single solar water-heating panel acceptable on the kitchen roof if it is facing south. When such win/wins are not available, it is best to provide basic information about the various eco-options and then leave it to the couple themselves to decide when you leave or when they get your report.

Confidentiality

Being allowed into someone's home as an eco-auditor is a real privilege and brings with it the same responsibilities that apply to any professional person who does home visits. It is essential that you respect the confidentiality of the people you are working with and do not reveal what you see and experience in their home unless you have their express permission. Breaking such trust would not only damage that particular working relationship but also harm the wider cause of eco-auditing if people felt that their privacy was not going to be respected.

While issues of privacy obviously do not affect an eco-audit of your own home that you are undertaking yourself, a business or organizational eco-audit does also require confidentiality. While I encourage companies to be transparent about their environmental performance – by including, for example, an annual eco-audit report in their annual accounts or by publishing it on an environmental section of their website – until legislation rules otherwise, it is entirely their prerogative whether they do so. Trust for eco-auditors and eco-auditing is essential if we are to spread the good practice of annual business eco-auditing as fast as we possibly can.

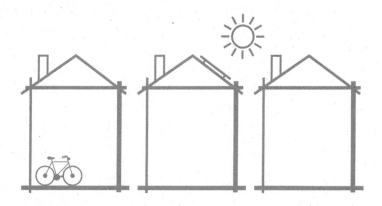

The home eco-audit

Having looked briefly at some of the ethics and relationship issues that might arise during an eco-audit, let us now get down to the basics of carrying out an eco-audit.

The eco-audit form

The first step towards getting a feel for the current environmental performance of your home is to fill out an eco-audit form (see pages 272–75 for sample form). This will help guide you on what areas to prioritize. It will also give you a feel for whether you are above or below average in terms of your carbon footprint and other environmental impacts. I cannot over-emphasize the usefulness of measuring your energy carbon footprints. It is one of the most powerful tools to inspire people to improve their performance, as it provides easily measured markers by which they can chart progress.

Discuss the purpose of the eco-audit

Having studied the eco-audit form, the next step, whether you are an outside eco-auditor or a family member, is to have a chat about what everyone is expecting from the process. For family members it is an opportunity to talk over why you think it will be useful to have a household eco-audit. If you are an outside eco-auditor, it will be an opportunity to get a feel for where the household is coming from, so that you can tailor your session in a manner that will be most useful to the client. After all, you will only have two or three hours to do the audit.

It will be impossible to cover absolutely every area and every aspect of a household's eco-performance, so you need to know what your priorities are to ensure that the final eco-audit report is as useful as possible in the specific circumstances. Do not expect to cover all the areas discussed in the following chapters in one eco-audit. However, you should have enough detail to deal with specifics in the areas of concern to your particular household.

In my experience, people have a range of reasons for hiring eco-auditors, the most common being that they want to do something to reduce the damage they are causing to the planet by how they live at home. Another popular reason for undertaking an eco-audit is to get advice on what renewable energy might be suitable for a particular home. I usually recommend a full eco-audit for someone wanting advice on renewables, as reducing the need for energy use in the first place will allow the renewables to provide more of the total energy used.

I have come across a number of other reasons for eco-auditing, including a desire to be independent of the national grid in case of disruption to energy supplies and the wish to reduce utility bills. People who have just bought a new home or who intend carrying out extensive renovations or redecoration will often want advice on how to do so in as eco-friendly a manner as possible. An understanding of people's motivations will guide your approach, so that it is in line with what those wanting the eco-audit are looking for.

It is during this introductory chat that I usually explain my overall approach to cutting carbon dioxide from energy consumption in the home:

• First 40 per cent of savings: lifestyle issues (how people actually use a home) – this will cost nothing and actually save money;

• Second 40 per cent of savings: basic energy efficiencies (energy-saving light bulbs, insulation, etc.) – this will involve some modest investment but will quickly start saving you money;

• Final 15–20 per cent of savings: renewable energy technologies – this usually involves considerable investment with payback varying from seven to 80 years.

Indoor walkabout

Once the chat is over, it is time to do the walkabout. It is usually best to start either at the top or the bottom of the house to avoid leaving any part out of the eco-audit. For the same reason, it is useful to go in strict circular order on each floor so that no room is omitted. Make notes as you go.

With the permission of the householder, it is important to open all wardrobe and cupboard doors. It is amazing what can be concealed in an innocent-looking small cupboard. I remember carrying out an audit of a large home in Hampstead. We were nearly at the end of the walkabout, with only the nanny's bedroom left. There was a small cupboard on the wall and I nearly did not bother to look in, when I remembered this rule. Inside, to my surprise, was yet another electric hot-water system (in addition to the two already identified on the walkabout), with no timer, so it was on 24 hours a day, and nobody knew what it actually was for! On another occasion, I found a load of storage cupboards in an attic. When I opened the final one, I discovered that the adjacent dormer window had never been sealed by the builder and so a 15-centimetre gap along one entire side of the window frame was allowing in a merciless cold gale in winter and was one of the reasons the room was so cold, despite being constantly and expensively heated with electric fires.

So, the moral of the story is to overlook no nook or cranny as you do the walkabout. Horror discoveries like those just described are what make eco-auditing extra worthwhile and fun, as they can mean significant financial and environmental savings for the householders. It is crucial to remember, as you do the walkabout, that you are entering people's private rooms, so keep asking for permission to open the various doors.

Outdoor walkabout

The format this will take depends on the type of property you are eco-auditing – whether it is an apartment, a terraced house or a detached mansion. But the usual advice applies: start at a point and go round in a circle, as far as the layout will allow, in order to ensure that you have seen and checked everything that could be relevant, from the downpipes to the contents of any garage or garden shed. Make notes as you go.

Eco-audit report

If you are an outside eco-auditor, the notes you made during your walkabouts will need to be typed up and sent to the household. If they have email, send the report (and any invoice!) that way, as that way you do not need to waste an envelope or use up postal van emissions. The household can print the report out on recycled paper or just read it on screen. (I run an almost totally paperless office, backing up my records on the web.)

Unlike in business eco-audit reports, I do not list the positive eco-friendly actions already being taken in domestic eco-audit reports. To do so would probably double the time spent drawing up the report, more often than not with no great benefit. However, if you are a household member making a report and you have the time, it might help to list them, as this would show that you appreciate what others are doing already and can build positive alliances within the family.

A sample home eco-audit report taken from a real-life London family, with identities concealed, is shown in the Appendix on pages 276–92. As you can see, in addition to the eco-audit form, it contains a list of suggestions to improve the environmental performance of the household, with a list of web resources or suppliers where relevant.

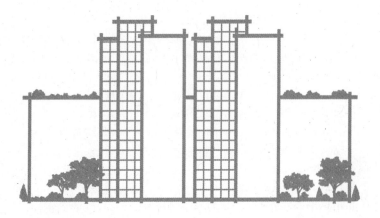

The business eco-audit

In many ways, the basic structure of a business or organizational eco-audit is similar to a home eco-audit, but there are some significant differences. These will be less pronounced if the client or your organization is a charity, a school or a not-for-profit or a governmental organization.

Business/organizational eco-audit form

The first thing to do is to email this form to your contact at the organization as soon as they have agreed to have an eco-audit, as it can take some time for a company to assemble the relevant information. If they have more than one premises, ideally a form would be filled in for each premises, then a summary form for the entire organization. One difficulty you will often find with a company's eco-audit form is the necessary information cannot be provided for a host of reasons: for example, the utilities are paid for by the landlord, especially if the company is in a multi-occupancy building. Not having access to the data needs to be included in the eco-audit report, so that the company can aim in future years to resolve this, maybe through negotiation with their landlord or even by installing sub-metering of their utilities, if practical.

Meeting with management

In many ways this has the same function as the initial chat with the householder in a home eco-audit, being an opportunity to find out what the company wants out of the eco-audit and for you to explain what the process will entail. It is, however, crucial in helping you to understand the structure and general organization of the company, so that you are able to design a procedure that will provide you with the greatest amount of relevant information within the time being paid for.

No two companies or management structures are the same. In fact some companies that I have eco-audited operated without any management meetings at all. Your job is not to judge their general management structures but to get a feel for how they are currently operating, so that you can meet key individuals in the organization who will be able to provide you with the information you need and also to act as the best promoters of change when the report is submitted and to ensure any management recommendations are relevant to their particular structures.

You should find out at this meeting the number, type and location of premises and the number of employees at each site. Sometimes, in larger organizations, you will not have the opportunity to visit every site, so, with the help of management, it is crucial to pick a selection of sites that provides the most comprehensive range of situations the company operates in.

Meeting with staff

It is essential to meet with staff and brief them fully about the eco-auditing process, giving them every opportunity to be included. After all, they are the people who will be responsible for implementing many of your practical recommendations, so if you win them over at the start, there is every chance of a successful conclusion once your audit is completed.

This meeting is the time to make allies and assure staff that you are not a threat. It is also your chance to identify key decision-makers who might not have been present at the management meeting.

Meetings provide a forum for staff to contribute their expertise on the environmental aspects of various operations within the business. No matter how much of an eco-expert you are, you can never know everything about an organization on the basis of a few hours' site inspection and meetings. If senior management are present, staff will see that the process and their contributions are being taken seriously, all of which will make the process more successful.

This is also the time for staff to ask questions, allowing the eco-auditor to allay or address any fears or concerns that they might have. It creates a space in which the wider global and environmental crises can be simply and briefly outlined. Ideally, this should be made relevant to what the company does, with an explanation of how staff can, through the eco-audit process, make a positive contribution to the alleviation of these crises.

Meetings are an opportunity for the eco-auditor to provide their own personal testimony. I always give a very short summary of why I got involved in saving the planet and what I have done to make my own life more eco-friendly. As I am in the process of asking people to change their current work patterns, it is only fair that I can demonstrate my own integrity in the area.

At the start of any meeting, it is important to assure your audience that this is not some sort of government inspection to see what they are doing wrong; instead, you are finding out what they already do well and to see how you can help them improve their environmental performance even further.

Depending on the structure and size of the organization, you may need more than one meeting with staff. For example, if phones have to be covered at all times, it might make sense to have two sessions in one day; if there are several premises, you might need to have a meeting in each. While you will rarely be able to have everyone in the company attend, it really is worthwhile within the time and budgetary constraints to try and reach as many people as possible.

On average, my meetings with staff take between half an hour and an hour. Ideally, I like to have carried out at least some of the eco-audit walkabout prior to the meeting, so that I already have some practical examples of the issues facing the company, which helps generate and inform discussion. Before opening up the session to questions, I usually take about 15 minutes to summarize the following:

• why the company has commissioned an eco-audit;

• what an eco-audit is;

• how I became involved in helping to save the environment;

• what is happening both globally and in the UK already as a result of the climate crisis and a brief summary of the dire predictions if nothing is done;

• practical measures I have taken in my own life to cut my eco-impact;

• what the eco-audit will actually entail for them;

• examples of issues I have already picked up on from my site walkabout prior to the meeting.

Detailed examination of the site/sites

This is necessary to examine current performance and identify areas that need attention. When you send the eco-audit form to management prior to arriving for the site visit, you should ask the company to identify the person to accompany you on your walkabout. Ideally, this should be the person responsible for the actual day-to-day maintenance of the premises. In some places there will be an actual facilities manager and in others it may simply be the office manager or even the chief executive's PA. In large organizations, the facilities management role (if it formally exists) can be located in a wide variety of departments, ranging from finance to operations. In your initial discussions with management prior to the audit, it is key that you identify where the most knowledgeable members of staff are to be found and ensure that they are available to accompany you on the day the site walkabouts are to take place.

Extra meetings

As you learn more about the company during the various meetings, you will start to identify key people with whom you can have productive one-to-one sessions. In a larger organization, you will probably need to meet at least one senior manager in each department, ideally the departmental head. Obviously it is crucial to make contact with the people who take the key decisions about purchasing, and then with the human resources department to talk through issues concerning employment and job specifications. In a charity, those involved in providing services to members or clients are important; in a delivery company, it would be those in charge of vehicle purchasing. Remember that every company will be different, so the people you need to meet will be different too.

Who is the key person in a company who can actually effect change on any single issue varies widely. To take an example, the decision about what kind of coffee a company uses can be made in an extraordinary range of places, from the chief executive, who may insist on a specific brand, the office cleaner, who goes to the local corner shop and buys whatever is available there, the stationery company, which supplies only one general brand of coffee, to the receptionist, who is asked to take charge of orders and gets a free gift from a delivery company if she orders certain brands. Trying to do even something simple like getting a company to change to an organic fair-trade brand of coffee can therefore take some detective work. This illustrates how alert you need to be as you carry out your meetings and do your walkabout with the facilities manager, picking up any bits of information that will help you identify the crucial decision-makers, no matter where they are in the company hierarchy.

Once you have identified this list of key people you need to have one-to-one meetings with, you will have to arrange when to see them. Sometimes they will be available when you have finished your walkabout, but if they are busy you might need to make an appointment. Ideally, though, everyone should have been informed about the eco-audit taking place and so be able to fit you in. These meetings will give you a chance to inform the key individuals you have identified about how the eco-audit relates to their particular field. You will need to ask them in-depth questions about current practice within their department and discuss any proposals for change that you are considering making in the report. This gives them an opportunity to let you know whether these make sense from their perspective and whether there are ways the ideas could be improved. In this way problems that may never have occurred to you can be aired and dealt with. Sometimes proposals that work well in other companies simply will not be practical in a specific case because of the particular needs of that organization. For example, I would usually recommend replacing anti-bacterial chemical-cocktail soaps with bars of soap with magnets to prevent melting and soiling. However, in hospitals, care homes and other such clinical-based residential units, for example, it is essential that staff use such hand-cleansers.

Final courtesy meeting

At the end of the walkabout in a small company or of the agreed series of walkabouts in a large company, it is only good manners to report back to senior members of staff prior to leaving and starting to prepare your report. They will expect you to be able to give a brief summary of what you have found, both positive and negative, and what proposals you are likely to be making. It is a good opportunity to explore the feasibility of some of the potential recommendations in the light of their knowledge regarding resources, willingness and time.

Eco-audit report

Prepare and send an electronic eco-audit report, listing current environmental performance, suggestions for improvement and proposed implementation strategy. A real-life business eco-audit can be seen on the 3 Acorns eco-audits website www.3acorns.co.uk.

Return visit

I try not to accept a commission for an organizational eco-audit from a company or charity unless they agree to include a return visit, usually between six months and a year later. There are a number of reasons for this. In the past, environmental audits often resulted in a company spending the time and financial investment, only for the report to end up languishing in an in-tray. This was not for any negative reasons but simply because the day-to-day crises that can arise in the running of an organization tend to overtake implementation of an eco-audit report.

If this has happened, a phone call from the eco-auditor to agree a date for the return visit will bring the report back to the top of the agenda. I am interested in actually improving a company's eco-performance and not just simply being paid to produce something that will end up gathering dust!

As well as ensuring that the report is not forgotten, the return visit serves other positive functions, including reinvigorating staff morale on the issue and solving any problems that may have arisen from implementation of the recommendations. For the eco-auditor it is also a crucial learning opportunity to see how your recommendations have succeeded. Often you will find that the company has come up with alternative versions of your recommendations that you will be able to apply in other companies, or you may discover challenges with the practical implementation of your recommendations that will better inform your future work.

Suggested return visit structure

1   Email or call your prime contact to agree date for return visit.

2   Request that the eco-audit report with comments on each of the recommendations be returned to you via email at least a week prior to the return visit. Comments should cover what action has taken place on each recommendation. It should state whether:

- it has been implemented;
- it is being implemented;
- a decision was taken not to implement, with reasons;
- a decision was taken to implement in future.

3   If a year has elapsed, then the eco-audit form should be refilled and sent to you.

4   On the day of the return visit, you should:
- have an initial meeting with the chief executive or owner to discuss progress or any concerns in general;
- go through the form in detail with a nominated member of the management team;
- have a meeting with as many staff as possible to discuss progress or issues that have arisen with them.

How to get your company interested in eco-auditing

If you want your company to have an eco-audit or you want to use this book to carry it out yourself, you will need to persuade the boss to go for the idea. There are a number of ways that you can go about this: you could arrange a meeting with your boss or your line manager to discuss the idea, submit the proposal if your company has an ideas box, raise it at a staff meeting or even with colleagues in the pub. Whatever approach you decide on, you will need some good reasons for why your company should listen to you. Here are some ideas:

■ A company eco-audit can save money by reducing waste across a range of areas, including water, food, lighting, heating, raw materials, purchasing, rubbish disposal, etc.

■ It can be good for morale, as staff who are already doing things at home to be more eco-friendly will welcome the opportunity to do so at work.

- It gives a positive message about the company to customers and clients.

- It can bring in new business from customers who want to work with an eco-friendly company (a recent survey in the UK by the Social Market Foundation found that over 82 per cent of consumers prefer to purchase goods and services from environmentally responsible companies).

- It can help retain current customers who might be tempted to go to more eco-friendly companies.

- It is the right thing for the company to do ethically, as the climate crisis is so severe that everyone should be doing their bit.

- It can help attract and retain good-quality staff. (Many graduates now state that they want to work only for companies with a sound ethical reputation.)

- It can identify new areas of eco-friendly business for the company to diversify into.

Chapter 3

Water

What price water?

Water is often the environmental issue that many people forget about. Until the 2007 floods in the UK, how many of us gave the water that flows magically from our taps a second thought? But that automatic flow carries a high environmental price. The water has to be extracted from rivers, lakes and aquifers, cleaned, often with chemicals, and then pumped to our homes. Of course, the more water extracted from rivers, the more concentrated any pollution left in them becomes. The average Briton uses 150 litres of tap water every day. You only have to imagine lifting the weight of 150 one-litre bottles of water to understand the energy required to pump such a heavy weight through kilometres of pipes. All of those water pumps are powered by electricity, the large majority of which is produced through the burning of oil and gas, resulting in the release of millions of tonnes of carbon dioxide.

In the UK alone, 4 million tonnes of carbon dioxide are released every year by the water industry, making it one of the largest single sources of climate chaos emissions in the country. Worldwide the water industry generates $450 billion annually – it is the world's second biggest industry. In view of increasing consumption and disastrously expanding populations, it is estimated that it would cost up to $180 billion to provide safe water for all of the world's population by 2025. This is three times what is actually currently being invested by water companies and governments in safe water provision. The UN has forecast that instead up to two-thirds of the world's population will be living in 'water-stressed' areas by 2025, with a terrifying seven billion facing water shortages by 2050. Over a billion people already lack access to clean water and 2.4 billion to sanitation. This has resulted in over half of hospital beds worldwide being occupied by people suffering from water-borne diseases.

In addition, there is the environmental cost to the lakes,

rivers, streams and aquifers from which we extract these huge amounts of water. Many of the world's greatest rivers no longer flow normally to the sea. For example, the formerly gigantic Yellow River in China now often fails even to reach the sea, while so much water has been diverted from the Rio Grande in the USA that it is now divided into two rivers, separated by a 400-kilometre dry section, and these, like the Colorado River, also frequently fail to reach the sea. In the UK over a quarter of the country's chalk rivers and steams are under threat; dozens of them dry up every summer, with all the negative consequences that has for the wildlife dependent on them.

In 2006 the World Commission on Water stated that 'Over 50 per cent of the world's major rivers are seriously depleted and polluted.' The consequences for wildlife can be catastrophic, with over one-fifth of all freshwater fish species facing extinction or actually extinct already. The freshwater Yangtze River dolphin is the latest creature to almost completely disappear. The massive reduction in fresh water reaching the major river estuaries makes them saltier and results in serious damage to unique wildlife habitats, which are dependent on the mix of fresh and salt water. In addition, in regions where over-extraction is causing the water table to fall, trees and plants are threatened as their roots have to go ever deeper to access the moisture they need for survival. Mammals like the otter and beaver, fish and insects, all of which depend on water for their survival, are affected when rivers and lakes suffer over-extraction or over-licensing, something which is happening in many countries, including in the UK.

Moreover, water resources themselves are under threat from climate change, with severe droughts like that experienced in the UK in 2005–6 expected to happen every three years on average. The Australian government, long a supporter of the US Bush administration in opposing action on the climate crisis, was forced by the extreme prolonged drought in 2006–7 to abandon their position and start taking urgent action in order to curb their carbon dioxide emissions. For the first time, they are starting to reuse their sewage water. The US Midwest, which experienced the devastating dust-bowl drought in the 1930s, is again threatened with severe droughts as the century progresses and the climate crisis worsens. In June 2007 whole swathes of the country suffered from some of the worst droughts since the 1930s, with over 80 per cent of Georgia, Nevada, Arizona, California, Florida, Alabama and Tennessee all affected. Even in Minnesota to the north-east, by the Great Lakes, over a third of the state was experiencing drought. So the more we build in a low-water lifestyle now, the better prepared we will be and the better we will be able to spread best practice in water efficiency to the developing world, as it becomes increasingly westernized.

Key facts on water

- UK CO_2 emissions due to transport of water are 4 million tonnes per year.

- In the UK average water consumption is 150 litres per day; in Berlin it is 100 litres.

- Average rainfall on a UK roof is 35,000 litres per year.

- The most modern water-efficient toilet uses only 4.5 litres per full flush and 2 litres per half-flush.

- A five-minute shower uses 30 litres and a bath uses up to 170 litres of water.

- A five-minute power shower can use up to 100 litres.

- An average hotel uses 650 litres of water per guest per day.

- A garden sprinkler uses 25,000 litres of water if left on for the entire day or just over 1,000 litres per hour.

- In the UK 24 per cent of water is lost from leaking pipes; in Germany it is 5 per cent.

- The UK government estimates that homes with water meters use 10 per cent less water than those without.

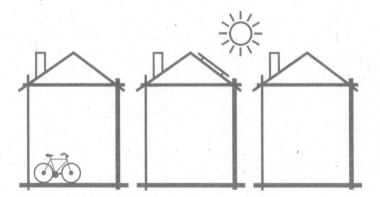

Home eco-audit

The first thing you need to look at if you are doing the household's eco-audit on water is the bill. This will have a number of useful bits of information. It will tell you first whether the bill is based on the amount of water used or on the rateable value of the property. If the bill tells you that the home is not metered, then look into whether the local water company will install one. In the UK most water companies will install meters for free. This will then mean that the household is accountable environmentally for the water it uses and it gives an economic incentive to cut out water waste and to fix leaking taps quickly. Obviously, if you have a large family or are wasteful with water, switching to a water meter could cause bills to rise, but for a small family living a water-wise lifestyle, bills could be reduced.

Kitchen/utility room

Check that the washing machine and dishwasher are water-efficient models. Naturally, the crucial time to consider this is when buying them. Invariably the most energy-efficient are the most water-efficient too, as most of the energy in these machines is used to heat the hot water. The EU's energy rating system, in which A++ means the most energy-efficient, will help to indicate best water efficiency as well. Inefficient washing machines and dishwashers use up to 100 litres and 40 litres respectively, whereas efficient brands use as little as 60 litres and 20 litres respectively. The UK consumer magazine *Which?* regularly does comparisons of the best washing machines to buy and includes water efficiency among its criteria.

While in the kitchen, gently ask household members about their tap habits. Leaving the tap running is a cardinal water-wasting sin, so check if anybody is doing so while rinsing dishes or washing vegetables. Using a bowl of clean water instead will save litres of water every time. You could also suggest using this water on the garden during dry spells in summer. Finally, while in the kitchen, do not forget to check the fridge to see if people are using bottled water or not.

You might use the following facts if you need to persuade people to switch from bottled to tap water. The environmental price for bottled water in the developed world is considerable. Despite having really excellent-quality drinking water in countries such as the UK, USA and Australia, literally billions of litres of plastic bottled water are drunk each year. This involves the shipping of more than 22 million tonnes of bottled water worldwide every year, with all the resultant carbon dioxide emitted by the ships, trucks and planes that unnecessarily transport them, without even mentioning the environmental cost of the plastic and cardboard packaging.

These billions of non-degradable and non-recycled plastic bottles will lie in landfill dumps across the globe for centuries to come. In the UK bottled water works out about a thousand times more expensive than drinking water from the tap, but people still buy it, despite the fact that UK water standards are among the most stringent in the world, exceeding those of the bottled water industry. In essence we are paying for packaging and marketing, not better health. Indeed, over 11 per cent of UK bottled water is 'purified water', which is nothing more than bottled reprocessed tap water.

One way to persuade people to change is to simply suggest filling a glass bottle with tap water and placing it in the fridge, so they still have access to cool water, or to carry a reusable flask with them.

Bathroom

Have a look in the toilets to see if the WCs are of the modern water-efficient variety, which use about 6 litres per flush, with ultra-efficient dual-flush WCs using only 4.5/2.5 litres per flush. Some pre-1960s cisterns used up to 20 litres per flush. If the WC has an older cistern put in since the 1960s, usually containing up to 9 litres, then you can reduce this in a number of ways. Fill a litre plastic bottle with water and place it in the tank; if the toilet continues to work well, add another one, and so on, until you find a balance between it working effectively and the amount of water used. A plastic bag device called a Hippo, which is often supplied by water companies, or a stone will do the trick equally well.

If the WC has no dual-flush action but has a handle rather than a push button there are devices that can be retro-fitted that will effectively convert it into a dual-flush version. One, called an Interflush, is fitted into the tank itself and causes the flushing to stop the second you let the handle go. For a pee it will use as little as 2 litres of water, which can save you up to 7 litres per pee. So, depending on how many pees a day your family has, you can save a lot of water simply by doing this.

While not a usual occurrence on an eco-audit walkabout, I did once come across a toilet cistern that was being filled with hot water instead of cold! For some bizarre reason, the plumber had connected the loo to the hot-water mains rather than the cold, thus wasting huge amounts of energy over the years it was in place.

Do not forget to check the taps and shower head. Aerating shower heads are now available which mix bubbles of air into the water drops, reducing the amount of hot water used by up to 30 per cent. Similarly, spray fittings on the head of the tap will reduce water flow by a similar amount, which is useful, as many people run the tap to wash their hands after using the toilet. If there is currently a screw fitting at the end of the tap, a spray one can be retro-fitted at minimal cost. When looking at the shower unit, do not forget to check if it is a power shower, which uses a pump to increase the pressure and thus the flow of hot water. A power shower uses up to three times the amount of water as a regular shower. Thus a ten-minute power shower could use 200 litres of water, nearly two and a half times the amount of water used in an average bath. If they have one, strongly recommend turning the power shower pump off if possible.

Outdoors

Eco-jargon refers to three types of waste water and you need to be able to explain the difference. First, there is rainwater, which obviously falls naturally. Secondly, there is grey water, which is the waste water from the various washing facilities in the house, such as the dishwasher and washing machine, shower and bath, and the water used in sinks. Thirdly, there is water-borne sewage from the toilet, referred to as black water.

For rainwater recycling, look to see if there are any downpipes suitable for water butts, if there are none already in place. Many water companies and local councils supply water butts and there are online companies offering a range of sizes and designs if you do not like the standard green plastic model. Then look to see if the layout of the building lends itself to the installation of a gravity-fed rain-harvesting system. This will store rainwater in a tank and then feed it through pipes for various household purposes. The most basic system simply supplies water to a WC, but at the other extreme there are expensive all-singing, all-dancing models that supply a fully plumbed-in non-drinking-water system in the house that runs parallel to the mains drinking-water supply. These elaborate models usually have a large tank buried in the garden and use an electric pump to get the water into the house. Ideally, the pump would be powered by a simple solar electric panel system. Similarly the filter systems vary from a simple wire sieve to screen out leaves to sophisticated modern filtration systems providing drinkable water. There are also intermediate systems emerging that use tanks attached to the rainwater downpipes from the roof, like a water butt but with a small pump inside which can pump water to an adjacent tap or toilet. The main caveat is that any system by law must not allow rainwater and mains drinking water ever to mix.

While investigating the potential rain-harvesting, also look to see if the outlet pipes from the shower and/or bath and the washing machine and/or dishwasher are suitable for the installation of a simple grey-water diverter. These are devices that divert the grey water from the outflow pipe into a hose when required. The grey water could then be used for washing the car or watering the garden in summer via a hosepipe. As with rain-harvesting, you can get sophisticated expensive grey-water systems installed that clean and store the grey water for non-drinking reuse around the house. While rainwater is generally comparatively very clean, grey water is normally contaminated with various things such as soap, detergents, human bacteria and food particles, making it more problematic for storage. Many sophisticated systems have to be programmed to dump the water if it has been stored for more than three days to avoid a build-up of bacteria. My preference is to avoid such complications and use only those grey-water systems that allow instant reuse for watering the garden or washing the car. Making our eco-friendly lifestyles as simple as possible is not a bad aim.

A zero-tech grey-water alternative, of course, is to use a trug in the shower. Rubber trugs with handles can now be bought cheaply and are ideal for showering in, and the water thus collected can be used manually to flush the toilet or water the garden.

Sprinklers and hoses

Lastly, but possibly most importantly, you need to impress on people the importance of not using garden sprinklers in the summer. A mains-connected sprinkler running at 1,000 litres per hour uses more in 11 hours than my home did in a whole year (10,220 litres). If you don't like to see lawns going brown in the summer, use grey water or rainwater from the water butt.

Tips for home water-saving

1 Do not let the taps run. Wash vegetables in a bowl rather than under a running tap. The dirt-enriched water can then be thrown on the garden in summer, doubling the water-saving. Likewise never leave the tap running when brushing teeth, rinsing dishes or shaving.

2 Have a short shower, not a long bath. A two-minute shower uses about 12 litres instead of the average 80-litre bath or

30-litre five-minute shower. Also turn down the flow of water while showering and turn it off when shampooing your hair.

3 Install a rain harvester. Use rainwater to fill your WC and for other non-drinking purposes around the house. If possible, install a simple large black plastic water tank and filter on the roof to collect the rain, which can then be piped using gravity to the WC. The pipe could have a tap coming off it in the bathroom to divert water for other types of cleaning around the house, such as washing the floor or windows.

4 Be economical with household washes. Wait until your washing machine and dishwasher are full before you use them.

5 Reuse shower or bathwater. Get a cheap, flexible rubber trug and stand in it when showering. This will collect the water, which can then be used for flushing the WC. You can also install a diverter from your outlet pipes to take the water for use elsewhere.

6 Install an Interflush. This device fitted to your WC will save litres of water each time you pee.

7 Get a water butt. Local councils and water companies have great offers – check their websites. Delivery is even free with many current offers and will include the easily installed (if your pipes are PVC) rain diverter.

8 Do not use a sprinkler. Allow grass to go brown in the summer. It is very resistant to drought and will recover with just one late-summer shower. Alternatively, convert some of the grassed area into shrubberies, which need far less maintenance

and water. Use rainwater from your water butt for watering plants. Water only the roots, when necessary, in the evening. If you water the leaves during the day, the sun will just evaporate the water and this does the plant no good. In dry spells, when the water butt runs dry, use waste grey water from the washing machine and shower to keep plants green and healthy.

9 Use a bucket, not a hose, to wash your car. A 15 mm hose uses over 100 litres in ten minutes, so most of the water is wasted. You need only 10 litres to wash and 10 litres to rinse the car.

10 Get a water meter. This encourages people to be even more water-efficient, as you not only help the environment but get the benefit of smaller bills as well. It ensures environmental accountability for the water used.

11 Buy only water-efficient washing machines and dishwashers. Some modern dishwashers use an astonishingly low 9 litres per full wash.

12 Do not power-shower. Power showers waste up to three times the amount of water of a regular shower.

Top ten plants for a water-efficient garden

- giant feather grass
- lavender
- olive tree
- pyracantha

- red hot poker
- rose 'Albertine'
- rosemary
- sage
- sun rose
- thyme

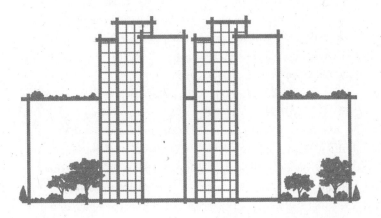

Work eco-audit

This will start in the accounts department, if there is one. You need to check whether the company is water-metered and, if so, what the annual consumption is, so you can get a feel of how big an issue water is for the company. Water bills in the EU are usually measured in cubic metres, each of which is the equivalent of 1,000 litres. So if your company used 40.3 cubic metres of water in the last year, this would be the equivalent of 40,300 litres. Then divide by 365 and the number of employees to get the number of litres per day per employee.

If the company has a water meter, ask whether someone is checking it regularly overnight. This is the most effective way to see if there are any undetected leaks on the premises. I made this recommendation to a charity I audited in south London. Having carried out the check, they found that a large amount of water had been lost overnight. They started looking for the leak but could not find it. They then went into the loft and found that the tank supplying the hot-water system was flowing continuously, which narrowed down the search. They eventually found a leak equivalent to a hot-water tap in full flow under the flooring on the ground floor. They reckoned it had been leaking for months, adding hugely to their heating and water bills.

Bathrooms

Companies use water in lots of different ways but the average office-based company usually uses it only in the bathrooms, cafeteria and/or kitchen. Occasionally there might be showers on the premises. The first things to look at are the toilets. Check whether there are old-fashioned continuously flushing urinals in the gents. This is one of the most frequent sources of very large water wastage on many premises. These older urinals can flush between 9 and 12 litres every quarter of an hour per stall or unit, twenty-four hours a day, all year round, whether the unit has been used or not and whether the premises is occupied or not. Thus they can waste up to a quarter of a million litres per year each! To my mind they should be made illegal as soon as possible. Presuming that the premises are water-metered, the cost of fitting controls (about £120) to ensure that flushing only happens after use would be recouped within about six months; after that they are saving money for the company and huge amounts of water, plus the energy used to pump it.

A more radical step, but one that major institutions such as the London School of Economics (LSE) and Kingston University have pursued, is to install waterless urinals. These work on the basis of retro-fitting into existing or new urinals a one-way valve system which allows the urine to pass through before closing, sealing and ensuring that there are no unpleasant odours. The LSE was so happy with their first trial of the waterless urinal, which they installed in the students' union bar toilet (which, needless to say, is well used!), that they retro-fitted valves to all 160 urinals throughout the college. They have now been in place for a number of years and the LSE reports far lower maintenance and water costs and cleaner-smelling gents' toilets. The cleaner smell is due to the fact that the odour from male urinals comes from the bacteria that grow on the deposited limescale that results from the interaction of water and urine. As this is eliminated in waterless urinals, they are therefore less smelly.

As in the home, check whether the WCs have dual-flush controls and, if they do not, suggest the retro-fitting of an Interflush or similar device, which will mean that the toilet stops flushing when the handle is let go. Also check the size of the cistern and suggest installation of plastic bottles or Hippos to reduce the size of each flush down to an amount that is still effective if they are larger than 6 litres. An office with 100 staff could save over £500 every year by installing Hippos if they have 9-litre cisterns on their toilets.

Spray taps are important in public toilets to reduce water wastage and in many cases installation of short-burst push-button taps is advisable, due to the frequency with which taps are left running in such toilets. One tap left running can waste huge amounts of hot or cold water in a small amount of time. The same applies to shower and bath controls in many institutions, where abuse of taps can be common. If there are showers on the premises, suggest the replacement of the shower heads with aerating shower heads.

Drinking water

Many businesses have water coolers supplied by large plastic bottles of water delivered by truck. These can be a big expense for an institution. There is a far cheaper and environmentally more benign way of supplying clean, cool water to staff. This is a mains-connected water cooler. They can be installed almost anywhere nowadays. This is because they connect the cooler to the water mains not by metal pipes but by a narrow plastic tube that looks very like electric wiring and can easily be laid along or through floors, walls and ceilings quickly and cheaply. At my former workplace we saved over £500 a year by replacing just one plastic bottle cooler with a mains-connected version. Imagine what a large HQ could save if it had a water cooler in every office. Eliminating these would eliminate the need for mountains of plastic bottles and for trucks emitting thousands of tonnes of carbon dioxide needlessly when transporting them around our cities.

While on the subject of water coolers, check to see whether disposable plastic cups are being used. One large national charity that I eco-audited was using over 72,000 of these every year in its HQ alone. I have never understood why organizations find it reasonable to supply china mugs for coffee but will use throw-away plastic cups for water. I will drink out of a mug to avoid using a throwaway cup if there is only a plastic-cup option. As far as I am concerned, a mug is a perfectly adequate receptacle for drinking water. If there is a system of bringing in your own mug, suggest the same for water glasses. Alternatively, the company could stock up with a batch from their local charity shop. If they will not move to reusable glasses for whatever reason, recommend that as a minimum they should sign up for a plastic-cup recycling scheme (e.g. Save a Cup) and use only recycled plastic cups.

Outdoors

Some companies will have a truck- or car-washing operation. There are commercial automatic car-washing systems on the market which recycle the water used, resulting in a reduction of up to 85 per cent in water use. If there are not any in place, ask if the company has considered installing one. While on this subject, some companies also spray-clean their vehicles, which means it is important to check whether the drains they are using are storm drains, which empty into nearby rivers or streams, or proper drains that can deal with contaminated waste. This is important, as it is illegal to allow contaminated water to pollute waterways.

Many premises will have a very large roof area on which hundreds of thousands of litres of rain will fall every year. If this is the case, a rain-harvesting system that could supply the toilets or other non-drinking uses should be seriously considered. In the UK information on large, professional rain-harvesting systems is available on the UK Rainwater Harvesting Association's website, which provides general information; Envir-Eau are manufacturers and installers of such systems.

If your company has industrial premises and uses significant amounts of water in processing, seek specialist advice on how to recycle the water. Many industrial processes that previously discharged large amounts of polluted water through the end pipe are now closed systems, whereby the pollution is filtered and removed and the water is recycled in the plant, reducing water bills and pollution.

Do not forget to tell your company about the government's scheme for water-efficiency investment, where the entire capital costs can be written off against taxable profits in the year of investment. Products that qualify for the scheme are listed on the government's website.

Questions to ask

- Do they have a water meter and, if not, are they willing to get one installed?

- Do they monitor water use annually?

- Do they have a water-efficiency programme in place?

- Have they provided information on how and why staff need to save water?

- Do they harvest rainwater falling on the building?

- Have they fitted dual-flush WCs?

- Do they have old-fashioned urinals in the gents' toilets?

- Do they have aerating shower heads fitted to any showers on the site?

- If there are car- or truck-washing facilities on site, do they have a water-recycling unit fitted?

- Do they use sprinklers or rainwater for watering any grounds around the premises?

Tips for saving water at work

1 Ensure that someone checks the overnight meter readings regularly to detect any leaks.

2 Ensure that all taps are fitted with aerators and flow regulators.

3 Install short–period push–button controls on taps and showers to eliminate staff wasting hot water and reduce water bills.

4 Get rid of any urinal controls that continuously flush and install waterless urinals instead.

5 If WCs are heavily used but are of an old, inefficient type that uses 12 litres per flush, consider replacing them with the most efficient models on the market.

6 Stop maintenance staff or contractors using garden sprinklers.

7 Mulch any flowerbeds in the grounds to reduce water-evaporation from roots.

8 Install a rain-harvesting system if there is a large roof area.

9 If there is an automatic vehicle wash on the site, ensure that it uses recycled water or have a company policy to use only commercial car washes that recycle waste water.

10 If the company uses water in any industrial processes, seek advice on how it could be recycled.

Chapter 4

Waste

Tackling the rubbish mountain

The figures in the eco-audit form will give you an idea of how much waste the household or business you are looking at is producing. People there may want to ask you why it is important to cut waste or to recycle, so again you will need some background information in order to be able to answer their questions.

It is hard to believe there is a connection between the innocent waste bin in the corner of the kitchen and the alarm bells ringing about the increasingly urgent global climate crisis. But the truth is that all the rubbish we throw away has in-built carbon emission costs, which include those involved in its manufacture, its transport to and from people's homes and workplaces, and its disposal, whether by landfill, incineration or recycling.

The average UK person throws away over 0.5 tonnes of rubbish every year. All of our combined overflowing rubbish bins in the UK add up to a shocking 180 million tonnes of waste. We spend nearly £3 billion every year collecting and disposing of this waste. And the problem is getting worse. Every year UK homes are producing 3 per cent more waste.

We have gone from an almost zero-waste society in our grandparents' time to a resource-hungry, throw-away consumer lifestyle. The consequences go far beyond the threat of climate change. To feed this huge waste stream, we are destroying rainforests in our search for more wood, metals and fossil fuels, mining conglomerates are polluting our rivers with toxic run-offs, and waste incinerators and rapidly filling landfill sites are emitting poisonous chemicals.

The UK government proposes to increase the number of toxic-waste incinerator plants from 15 to over 115. People are not exactly queuing up to have one in their communities, which is not surprising. These toxic-waste plants nearly always end up in poor neighbourhoods rather than rich ones. With current landfill sites scheduled to be almost completely full by 2015, urgent action is needed to reduce waste.

The EU is trying to tackle this wasteful and dangerous disposal culture, but businesses and households need to help as well, by reducing and recycling the waste they dump. New EU laws are at long last forcing the motoring and electrical-goods industries to recycle their cars, fridges, TVs and so on when they come to the end of their useful lives. Nine million cars are currently dumped every year across the EU. The new directive means that these will now have to be recycled.

On the list of European recycling rates, the UK is languishing near the bottom at 28 per cent. Germany, Austria, Switzerland and the Netherlands already have rates of over 50 per cent; Flanders in Belgium has an inspiring 71 per cent. The UK puts more waste into landfill sites than Germany, France and the Netherlands put together. We dump more than five billion glass bottles every year, glass that could easily be recycled; in addition, we dump another 460,000 tonnes of plastic bottles. Local councils will soon be fined £150 by the EU for every tonne of waste over a set target they dump into landfill.

There is some good news, though. For example, the newspaper industry in the UK has increased its use of recycled paper from 41 to 75 per cent in just ten years. While millions of households now recycle, reducing the amount of waste we produce in the first place is crucial, as even recycling results in carbon dioxide emissions. Over nine out of ten UK households now recycle at least one item every week, whereas ten years ago it was only one in ten.

Avoiding waste

Not producing waste in the first place is the most important thing. Households, businesses and local government have not given as much thought to reducing waste in the first place as they have to recycling. Even organic food frequently comes over-packaged. The Soil Association is now adding standards for sustainable packaging to its organic-certification criteria. One of the most important aims of your eco-audit walkabout on waste should be to get across the importance of avoiding as much waste creation as possible. Even recycling has emission costs, in terms of both transport and reprocessing into new products, though obviously the latter is less costly than creating goods from raw materials: for example, making an aluminium can from recycled aluminium uses less than one-twentieth of the energy used for one made from raw bauxite.

Ideally, homes and businesses should aim in the near future to have only recycling and compost bins, with no bins for unrecycled waste. The jargon for this is a zero-waste lifestyle. We need to make the concept of dumping waste really unfashionable. A genuinely modern consumer society would be a mirror image of a forest, where all the leaves and wood are continually recycled into new plants and trees, with all our household and business waste seen as raw materials to be recycled into new products. Nature has no waste and neither should we. With the huge increase in demand for resources from the newly emerging industrial giants India and China, such a dream is essential if we are to maintain life as we know it on the planet. The window of opportunity is closing fast, but if governments, businesses and individuals tackle our waste mountain urgently, carbon dioxide emissions can be massively reduced.

Why we need to cut our waste and recycle

- Disposal of waste creates CO_2 emissions from trucks and from incinerators if local councils burn their waste.

- Rotting food waste in landfill dumps creates methane, which is 21 times more powerful as a climate-changing gas than CO_2.

- Nobody likes living next to a huge new dump, so we are running out of landfill space; in southern England all existing landfill dumps are expected to be full by 2010.

- Disposal of waste costs literally billions of pounds in wasted taxes and charges (over £4 billion in 2006), money which could be better spent elsewhere.

- Dumping valuable metals, of which there are only limited amounts on the planet, is unfair to the next generation and to the millions in developing countries who want a better lifestyle and so need access to products using such metals.

- The increasing amount of incineration turns household waste into toxic ash due to the extraordinary mix of metals and chemicals now found in domestic waste bins.

- The manufacture of recycled paper, cans, bottles and aluminium saves enormous amounts of energy and water compared to making them from raw materials, which means that recycling reduces CO_2 emissions.

- Recycling reduces the need to import millions of tonnes of raw materials, again reducing CO_2 emissions.

- It is estimated that the average consumer spends over £500 on packaging each year, most of which is immediately dumped.

- Recycled resources provide the raw materials for a whole host of products, from aggregate for road building made from recycled glass to plastic composting bins and water butts.

- Mining for minerals produces huge amounts of toxic substances and destroys beautiful natural habitats across the globe, often destroying the way of life of indigenous people.

- Recycling saves huge amounts of CO_2. For example:
  - recycling an aluminium can uses about 5 per cent of the energy used to make a can from scratch;
  - recycled paper saves up to 50 per cent of the energy used for virgin paper;
  - recycled glass saves 25 per cent of the energy used for new glass.

- Recycling eliminates the huge waste associated with producing raw materials. For example:
  - every tonne of paper recycled saves 30,000 litres of water;
  - every tonne of recycled glass saves 112 tonnes of raw materials used to make new glass.

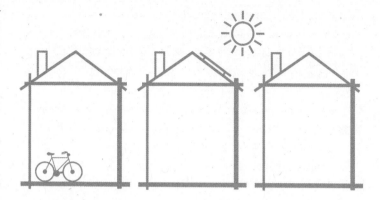

Home eco-audit

Having looked at the eco-audit form, you will already know how much waste is being produced. Now you want to set about lowering that amount. One of the key ways of doing this is to avoid items that are disposable instead of multi-use.

Kitchen

Starting in the kitchen, watch out for disposable kitchen towels instead of washable cloths. Recently, there has been a crazy trend to use disposable anti-bacterial wipes for everything from washing the floor to cleaning counter tops. Apart from the irresponsibility of using anti-bacterial products outside of hospitals or clinical situations, this has led to a totally unnecessary waste stream. Instead, buy washable cloths, which can even be made from recycled materials. For example, E-cloths have versions suitable for cleaning glass and mirrors, as well as for washing sinks and counters. Check the cleaning cupboard to see if over-packaged dishwasher tablets are being used and, if they are, replace them with dishwasher gel. Also you should check to see if there are any local outlets that refill washing-up liquid bottles: eco brands such as Bio-D are occasionally available like this.

Take a look in the food cupboards to check packaging. If any cereals come in a box with a bag inside, this is unnecessary. You should aim to buy products that have a maximum of one layer of packaging. Even better, some local shops allow you to take your own bags and fill up with loose cereals, dried fruit, pulses, rice, etc., which eliminates all the packaging.

Another thing to look out for in cupboards is packs of bottled water. With some of the safest and cleanest tap water in the world, it is wasting energy and resources to buy bottled water in the UK. If people insist they like bottled water because it can be kept cool in the fridge, suggest that they simply fill a bottle with tap water and place it in the fridge.

If you have lots of bottles or cans of fizzy drinks, think about swapping to concentrated organic juices, which will be healthier and also cut down on the number of cans and bottles to get rid of. Even better is to drink tap water and eat real organic fruit instead of juices, most of which come in Tetra-Paks, or other cartons, which are very difficult to recycle as they are made of a mixture of materials, such as cardboard, plastic and aluminium lining.

People do not realize that by gulping litres of orange juice they are consuming far more fruit than they would ever normally eat. This unnecessary consumption has led to a massive expansion of water-greedy orchards in many dry countries, depleting precious water aquifers and porous rock containing water that can be used to supply wells.

Also look out for things like pre-packed TV dinners, which have contributed to much of the recent rise in packaging waste. Think about swapping to an organic fruit and veg box scheme, most of which use returnable packaging, and then try to cook from scratch more often with simple but healthy ingredients.

Stuffed inside cupboards may also be heaps of plastic

shopping bags. Take you own bag when you go out shopping. Approximately 17.5 billion plastic bags are given away by supermarkets each year in Britain, up to four billion by Tesco alone. This is obviously crazy. The Scottish Executive calculated that you could drive a kilometre on the oil used to make eight plastic bags. I estimated that with the oil used for Tesco's bags I could drive 500 million kilometres, if I had a car that is!

Bathroom

First of all, check that the loo paper is made from recycled paper. There is no point in recycling paper if nobody buys the products made from it. We would just end up with more huge mountains of unused recycled materials!

Do not be misled by commercial spin into feeling that you have to buy plastic-bottled anti-bacterial soaps. These should only be used for clinical reasons, otherwise we are risking the rise of antibiotic resistance. Antibiotics are a precious gift to humanity from science and should not be squandered because some soap company wants to scare you into buying unnecessary products.

Rather than using disposable razors and cans of shaving foam, you should choose razors with replaceable blades and use a shaving brush instead. There are toothbrushes now available with replaceable heads, which means that millions of plastic toothbrush handles do not have to be thrown away – every eight toothbrush handles wastes about 1 kilometre's worth of oil. There are also toothpick-type implements with replaceable heads that can be used over and over again if you need to take extra good care of your teeth and gums in addition to brushing them. They are called Proxabrushes and Oral B and GUM make versions of them.

If you feel able to broach the subject – and it will have to be done with tact and gentle humour – the area of female sanitary products needs to be looked at, because every year millions of such products are disposed of. Each woman will throw away over 10,000 towels and tampons in her lifetime. There is now a product on the market called a Mooncup, which is basically a small silicone rubber cup that will collect menstrual blood, which can then be emptied and replaced. It avoids all the toxic-shock dangers and discomforts of traditional sanitary products. Quite a few female friends have reported their delight to me after switching over.

If you have a baby, are you using real nappies? Switching to real nappies will save over £600, as the average baby goes through up to 6,000 nappies. This is more than the price of a new washing machine!

Recycling

Somewhere on the eco-audit walkabout you should come across where people store their recycled cans, paper, bottles, etc. If they are not recycling, you will need to ask why. A common response is that they are confused about what can and cannot be recycled, as different councils naturally have different systems. This is really easily solved, as every local council has a recycling section on their website that will explain clearly what and how householders can recycle in their particular area or you can simply call them to find out or visit www.recyclenow.com. The other reason you will be given is that all recycled materials get dumped anyway. This is a myth that originated in the early days of paper recycling, when Germany introduced a new law requiring compulsory recycling for industry. As the infrastructure was only being set up, it meant there was suddenly a glut of waste paper in Europe for about 18 months. This resulted in a sharp fall in the price paid for waste paper and made it uneconomic for a short period, leading to some collected paper being dumped. However, that was over ten years ago; there is now a better recycling system in place and none gets dumped.

It is true, however, that due to the lack of a sufficiently large market as yet, some of the UK's recycled materials, such as plastics, get exported to countries like China, which have a good infrastructure in place for using recycled materials. China pays three times the UK rate for recycled plastic, which is shipped back there in empty container ships that brought manufactured goods to Europe. While not ideal, until such time as consumers and manufacturers in the UK buy and use more recycled materials, it is far better for this to happen than to simply dump the stuff in our bins or for China to use far more fossil fuels to produce new plastic.

Outdoors

As the eco-walkabout usually ends outside, now is the time to check whether people are composting their food waste, such as leftovers and peelings from fruit and vegetables. Obviously you should also check that households with gardens are composting their garden waste. Using trucks to take away compostable materials from houses with gardens is another silly way to waste time and energy. However, if people do not have a garden, suggest they look at their local council's website, as there may be a composting collection whereby the council will provide a small covered bucket and then collect it weekly. If there is no such council scheme where you are, you could always copy a friend of mine who lived in a flat with no garden. She took her compostable waste down to the local allotment and gave it to mates there for use on their vegetables.

For people living in blocks of flats, it is worth suggesting that they approach the building management about creating a communal composting site if the flats have gardens around them. Even if they do not agree to do this, the management might be persuaded to at least start composting their garden waste on site.

Types of composting

There are several different types of composting.

Traditional compost heap in garden

Before domestic waste collections became normal, households with large gardens usually simply dug a hole at the bottom of the garden, tipped all the food waste into it and covered it with earth when full, then started another hole. I remember this happening in my parents' house during the 1960s in a small rural town in Ireland. Even simpler is to dump all the leaves and grass cuttings under the shrubbery at the end of the garden – nature will take care of the rest.

Wooden-frame compost heap

The simplest of the structural composting systems, this is a square wooden frame with access at the bottom to dig out the composted material and place it on the garden.

Wormery

This is a sealed container with worms in, with a lid at the top and a side tap to take out liquid rich in nutrients for potted plants, etc. The worms speed up the composting process by digesting organic materials placed in them. The advantage is that the wormery does not need to be placed in soil, as the liquid can be drained via a tap, so even people in flats with balconies can use them. They are suitable only for kitchen waste; they are not big enough for garden waste and you have to make sure the worms do not die.

Plastic composters

The most common of these is effectively a plastic barrel with an open bottom that you place on soil to allow liquid to disperse. There is access at the bottom to allow you to dig out composted materials. You cannot use animal waste.

You can buy a rodent-proof plastic barrel with a metal cage underneath to prevent rodent access. Alternatively, there is the rotating composter, which is usually placed on sideways on a frame, with hatch-door access for putting in waste and digging out compost. There is a handle to turn the barrel to aid mixing of materials. This is suitable for meat products as it is also rodent-proof.

Finally, there is the Green Cone. This is a small plastic cone dug into the soil which, because of its shape, speeds up the composting process due to a greater build-up of heat. The amazing advantage it has above other types of composting is that is can take all food waste, including dairy, meat and fish. It uses the heat of the sun and specially added naturally occurring bacteria to speed up decomposition, helping to avoid the methane release that occurs in landfill. The other plus is that your refuse bin will no longer be smelly or dirty and so you will not need bin liners any more either.

Tips for a low-waste lifestyle

1 Buy your fruit and veg from an organic box scheme that uses returnable containers and also buy milk in returnable bottles.

2 Stop buying disposable products such as paper handkerchiefs, razors, kitchen towels, plastic cups, etc.

3 Get a wood-burner to burn your own and your neighbours' untreated waste wood.

4 Avoid buying packaging that is hard to recycle, such as Tetra-Paks, or is excessive, such as double-wrapped boxed and bagged muesli.

5 Keep a folded plastic bag in your rucksack or handbag for shopping.

6 Shop in local farmers' markets, where you can put all your produce into reusable bags.

7 Dispose of unwanted furniture, clothes, books, etc., via local second-hand stores, charity shops or on your local Freecycle website.

8 Buy a vermin-proof Green Cone composter that can take all your food scraps and green garden waste.

9 Recycle everything that you can. Your local council will have a recycling section on its website that will tell you what and where you can recycle locally.

10 Reduce landfill waste by buying reused or antique furniture, sourcing building materials from architectural salvage yards, buying products made from recycled materials and local charity shops.

11 Sign up for the Mail Preference Service to stop junk mail, which makes up 4 per cent of our paper waste.

12 Use real nappies rather than disposables, which take up to 500 years to decompose and make up 3 per cent of total domestic waste.

13 Get a battery recharger. Rechargeable batteries can be reused up to a thousand times. Batteries are one of the most toxic things you can throw in a landfill, so ensure that they are recycled at the end of their life.

The final thing to stress is the importance of keeping track of how much unrecycled waste is being produced. If people actually measure how much they produce, they will notice the difference as they switch to a low-waste lifestyle, which can be very rewarding.

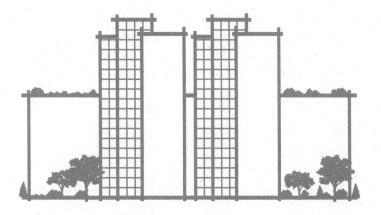

Work eco-audit

As with the home waste eco-audit, this should start by looking at the entry on the eco-audit form to see how much waste the company is producing. With most office-based companies, the waste streams will be similar to that of a household, but probably with a much smaller proportion of food waste and a much larger proportion of paper waste. The additional issue for companies is that a lot more legislation covers the way waste is dealt with than applies to the average householder. It is important therefore that the company is aware of this legislation, even if conforming with it does not necessarily improve its eco-performance.

Unlike that for households, the UK's waste collection for

businesses is 100 per cent commercial, and for smaller businesses recycling is still voluntary. Some local councils may provide a commercial service, but it has to be paid for, and several large corporations are involved in the collection and disposal of waste from businesses. There are EU legal requirements however on some of the largest companies to increase the level of waste recycling.

There is no requirement on most offices to recycle any of their waste. What is more, unlike the case with most homes, there is usually no recycling service provided by councils for businesses, although this has now finally started to improve. Basically the government has responded to voter pressure in providing home recycling services, but there is no such pressure coming from businesses, so the government is doing very little. This despite the fact that business waste makes up 40 per cent of the total waste stream, compared to 10 per cent from domestic houses; the other 50 per cent comes from the construction and mining industries. The neglect of business recycling by government is a shame, and it also creates problems for eco-auditors, who, when advising clients to recycle their waste stream, will sometimes be told they have tried but failed to find anyone providing a commercial recycling service in their area.

So, when doing the waste eco-audit, you will have the added challenge of persuading a company that it is important to find the budget to start recycling if a service is available locally. The plus point is that they are already paying for waste disposal, which means it is a question of highlighting the value of recycling for all the reasons given above, but also for the sake of the company's reputation and staff morale. Many staff who are used to recycling at home feel frustrated if they are unable to recycle at work, so if the employer remedies this, they will feel much happier. Small to medium amounts of money can also be saved if waste is eliminated in the first place.

Ideally, you should be able to recommend a commercial recycling company that operates in the area. If not, you could contact the recycling officer at the local council, who may have a list of such local organizations.

Canteen

If there is a canteen, this will be a source of considerable amounts of waste. Check whether they are using disposable crockery and cutlery and suggest replacing them with reusable items instead. This will have a staff implication, but it is important to raise the issue and include it in your eco-audit report recommendations. Also look to see if they are providing napkins from recycled paper and if there is tap water readily available rather than bottled water. If there are canned and bottled drinks on sale, check that there are recycling facilities for them and, if there are, advise them to avoid stocking Tetra-Paks or other juice cartons, which are very difficult to recycle.

Offices

In the offices check whether plastic cups are provided for the water fountain and, if they are, suggest these are replaced with glasses. If there is a problem with washing up, suggest each member be responsible for their own glass, as they are often responsible in some companies for their own mugs. In the office kitchen look out for sugar packets and, if they are used, suggest replacing them with sugar shakers, filled with organic fair-trade sugar of course!

You need to check if they have a full range of recycling in place and, if they have, how it is organized and whether staff know what can be recycled and how. When I do my waste walkabouts, I often find that staff are confused about what and where they should place items for recycling. Putting up notices around the premises, especially beside any recycling bins, will sort this out.

Another useful tip, if there is a paper recycling system in place already, is to reverse the usual office bin system. Most companies with paper recycling systems have a central paper recycling bin and then each desk has an individual waste bin (usually lined with a plastic bag) for non-recyclables. This does not make much sense, as most waste from an office desk is paper-based and, human nature being what it is, people find it easier to just dump the paper in the bin beside them. I suggested this reversal to a charity I eco-audited in south London and they contacted me excitedly a while later to let me know that since they had made this change the paper recycling rate had shot up by more than 500 per cent almost overnight. This of course then led them to wonder where all this paper was coming from and so they started a process of eliminating the waste paper production in the first place. For example, they cancelled duplicate copies of magazines they were receiving and by switching the photocopier to automatically print double-sided, they reduced their paper use by over 43 per cent.

Key waste legislation issues for companies

It is important for companies to realize that various aspects of how they dispose of waste are covered by both EU and national legislation, which is constantly evolving. In the UK the government website provides information on environmental legislation that could affect the company you are eco-auditing. For example:

• legal requirements on packaging recycling: this covers companies with a turnover of over £50 million handling over 50 tonnes of packaging;

• EU waste electrical and electronic equipment: provides duty for electronic goods to be recycled at the end of their life (the UK currently dumps over 100 million TVs, mobile phones, stereos and computers annually);

• legal requirement for the company/person removing your waste collection to be licensed to do so;

• legal requirements for disposal of certain hazardous products, including waste oil, fluorescent lights, batteries and computer monitors (for advice on how to dispose of these items locally, contact the local council's waste disposal department).

Waste as raw materials

The purpose of the waste eco-audit is to help advise a company how to reduce their waste in the first place and how to recycle what they cannot avoid creating, so that ideally they end up with zero waste being dumped. For many companies, to achieve this they need to change how they look at waste. Instead of seeing it as waste, they need to look at it instead as a potential resource, if not for their company, then maybe for another company. Some paper mills have recently slashed their waste production when, instead of dumping the sludge that was left over after the paper-making process, they started drying it out and using it as a fuel to power their paper mills. The Canadian Catalyst Paper Mill has done this and succeeded in reducing not only their waste stream but also cut their carbon dioxide emissions by a tremendous 71 per cent over 15 years.

There are a number of organizations now popping up to act as waste–resource marriage brokers, as I call them. They enable companies with waste streams they have no current use for to make links with companies that could use those waste streams for their own purposes. In the UK, Envirowise (www.envirowise.gov.uk) should be able to advise you on any local or regional organizations doing this in your area. So, keep an eye out as you do your waste walkabout for any large unrecyclable waste streams that might be useful to other companies.

Questions to ask

- Are they using disposable crockery or plastic cups?

- Have they a full recycling system in place for paper, cardboard, glass, cans and plastics?

- Do they have composting facilities on site?

- Do they use disposable items such as paper towels or antibiotic counter wipes?

- Do they have a waste-reduction policy in place?

- Are all hazardous waste items disposed of legally?

- Do they recycle their IT equipment?

- If there is a recycling system in place, are all the staff aware of what and how to recycle?

- Do they monitor how much unrecycled waste is dumped each year and have they targets for its reduction?

- Are they moving towards a paperless office (e.g. keeping electronic copies rather than paper copies or implementing electronic invoicing)?

Chapter 5

Nature: working on the wild side

The natural world and eco-auditing

Nature is not the first thing people think about when they decide to get an eco-auditor in, but if there are grounds surrounding a home or premises, then the eco-audit should include how that space is being used to either help or hinder nature. Indeed, even if there are no grounds, there are still things that you can do to help nature. When I worked in an office in Victoria, central London, my boss, Jack Haslam, who was the finance director, brought in a bird-feeder to hang outside the window. Within weeks it had become a Mecca for great tits, which gave us endless pleasure over the following years. As usual, if you are going to cover this area in the eco-audit, you will need to be able to answer questions about why it is necessary to deal with such issues in the home or workplace.

As with the global climate crisis, the facts about the current state of the natural world are really alarming. There is almost no part of the globe that is not now recording massive drops in the numbers of wild animals, plants and birds. Indeed, scientists state that we are in the middle of the fifth great extinction period since the planet began, over 3.5 billion years ago. Some believe our destruction of species is so serious they call it biocide. Some 40 per cent of the 40,000 animal, plant and bird species examined by the 10,000 scientists of the World Conservation Union are now at risk of being eliminated forever from the planet. Increasingly, people are realizing that our food security and future economy depend on there being healthy animal, bird, insect and plant life on the planet. Humans are, after all, animals and so depend on nature for food and even oxygen; we are as interdependent with the wider natural world as any other organism. The pollination of food crops by bees alone is estimated to be worth over £50 billion worldwide. Yet various species of bee are already in deep trouble as we spray and destroy ecosystems across the globe.

One of the most amazing facts about nature is how things are interlinked in mutual support systems, but within that miracle also lies a vulnerability, because if one of the cornerstone species is knocked out, a whole host of other life forms dependent on it can also disappear. The Scottish pine forests are a classic example. Over the centuries the natural mammal predators of the Scottish Highlands, such as the brown bear, lynx and wolf, were hunted to extinction. This meant there was nothing to keep deer numbers in check. Thus the deer had free rein to eat the emerging young tree saplings to their hearts' content. This has meant that over a century later the remaining segments of the once proud forest are now made up of ageing pine trees, as almost no young trees have been able to survive into maturity. The organization Trees for Life is now trying to preserve the remaining segments by protecting saplings from the deer and other conservation and biodiversity measures. With the trees went a whole ecosystem of wild flowers, plants, animals and birds. Some scientists now fear that such damage is being done on a global scale, presenting a threat as dangerous to humanity as the climate crisis.

In the UK, the RSPB reports that birds are now nesting up to nine days earlier than they were 90 years ago. With the warmer winters, the usual spring burgeoning of insect populations, so crucial to the survival of many migrating bird species at nesting time, is happening earlier, making it difficult for migrating birds to ensure that they are here at the right time to feed their chicks. As these eco-rhythms fall out of sync, the danger of catastrophic collapses in bird populations increases.

Species in danger

- One in four mammals are threatened with extinction.
- One in three amphibians are threatened with extinction.
- One in five bird species are threatened with extinction.
- One in three conifers are threatened with extinction.
- Over three-quarters of flowering plants are threatened with extinction.
- 52 per cent of insects are threatened with extinction.
- More than three species a day are eliminated from the planet forever, as rainforest destruction continues unabated.
- Bee diversity has fallen by over 80 per cent since 1977 in north-west Europe.
- Insect-pollinated wild flowers in north-west Europe have fallen by 70 per cent since 1977.
- Entire species are being wiped off the face of the earth by human destruction at a rate between 100 and 1,000 times higher than is natural.
- The number of threatened animal species has risen from 5,200 to 15,500 in the last ten years, demonstrating the alarming speeding up of destruction.

Some shocking facts

- Numbers of the Saharan dama gazelle have fallen by 80 per cent in the last ten years, leaving just over 200, due to rising temperatures in the desert and poaching.

- The total number of polar bears is 25,000 and is predicted by US government scientists to fall by two-thirds by 2050, due to the rapidly disappearing summer Arctic sea ice.

- Numbers of Bengal tigers have fallen from over 20,000 in 1957 to just over 1,000.

- Some 65 species of harlequin frog have disappeared in the last 30 years.

- Grauer gorilla numbers have plummeted by over 90 per cent since 1997 to just 2,000. There are only 700 mountain gorillas left and only 200 cross-river gorillas. The UN estimates that all these could be gone in ten years.

- Numbers of rock-hopper penguins on the Falkland Islands have fallen by 30 per cent in just five years.

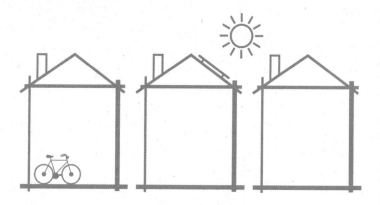

Home eco-audit

The main nature issues on the home eco-audit walkabout will obviously be found outside the house, in the garden. The fact that there are 15 million gardens in the UK means that every one of these provides an opportunity to either help or damage local wildlife or nature. They cover over 300,000 hectares, which is more than all our nature reserves put together. You will need to look at two areas in particular. First, are any toxic garden chemicals being used that are poisonous to wildlife. Second, what proactive steps are being taken to encourage more wildlife in the garden.

Different issues affect front and back gardens. Yet another environmentally destructive outcome of car ownership is that many front gardens have been turned over to concrete slabs for car parking. However, you will often find that even in front gardens that are too small for car parking, the little pocket of nature has been concreted over or covered in gravel. Gravel at least allows water to soak into the earth beneath, but concrete contributes to severe flooding problems with rainwater during storms. Even if your home does not have its own front garden, you could approach the local council's tree officer and request a street tree, if there are none there already. If you live in a block of flats with a small garden in front of them that could benefit from having a tree being planted there, either approach the apartment owners requesting them to plant trees or obtain permission to plant them yourself.

When you get to the back garden, it really is important to check the garden shed, as it is there you will find any chemical pesticides or herbicides that people may be using. Over 30,000 tonnes of pesticide are sprayed on the UK's gardens and farms every year, poisoning insects and birds, and polluting our waterways. Every 'safe' pesticide seems to get banned eventually once previously unknown threats to human health emerge. In the latest study by Professor Ascherio of the Harvard School of Public Health, those exposed regularly to pesticides were found to have up to a 70 per cent increase in incidence of Parkinson's disease.

Moss peat

You may also find half-empty bags of moss peat. The use of moss peat in our gardens over the last 80 years is one of the great and totally unnecessary crimes against nature in the UK. Moss peat is the very fertile top layer of soil stripped from our native peat bogs. Over 93 per cent of them have been lost already, resulting in the almost total destruction of a unique and valuable ecosystem, with all the loss in an exciting variety of birds, animals, plants and insects that entails. This has also resulted in a major release of carbon dioxide stored in such bogs. It is criminal to continue using moss peat in our gardens when there are plenty of other ways of maintaining fertile garden soils naturally, such as using the compost readily available from our kitchen waste.

Wild flowers

While in the garden, have a look to see if there is room to plant more trees (fruit trees have a double advantage in that they can also help to reduce food miles), to make a nicely designed wild-flower meadow or simply to hand an area over to wilderness. Obviously, they will also absorb and store CO_2 from the atmosphere.

On an eco-audit visit I made to a home in Surrey in 2006, the owners took me out into their very large front garden, about half of which they had planted up as a wild-flower meadow. I thought it looked really nice, especially the way they had made a feature of it by surrounding it with a neat boundary of cut grass, but then they told me to slightly close my eyes and look closely at the air above the flowers. I gasped when I realized that the space was absolutely thronged with an amazing range of insects, from bees and wasps to butterflies and dragonflies, plus a host of others. It really was a thrilling sight, of which the owners were justly proud of.

With one in five of Britain's wild flowers now under threat of extinction, we need to persuade as many people as possible to follow their lead where practical. Such gardens will also be crucial in helping to save Britain's butterflies: their populations have declined by over 70 per cent in the last 25 years, with some varieties approaching extinction.

Garden habitats

If you do not already have a wildlife pond, check to see if there is a good place to install one. The number of ponds in Britain has fallen from 1.2 million in 1880 to less than half a million today, with the resultant loss of habitat for insects, frogs, newts, toads, etc. A new pond will quickly attract a huge range of wildlife to the garden. It is important for one side of the pond to be sloped, as otherwise the amphibians might drown if they cannot get out. This happened to me a number of times when I inadvertently left a bucket with water beside the rain barrel: frogs had jumped in to get at the water, but died there because they could not get out again afterwards.

If you have bare garden walls, allow ivy to colonize it. Ivy provides food for butterflies and bees, while birds love its winter berries; it is home to a whole host of insects and is even used as a nesting site by some birds. In a similar way, allowing wood to rot in a damp, dark corner of the garden instead of getting the council to take it away will create a space where hedgehogs, frogs and newts can over-winter. The wood will also be good for a host of insects, including stag beetles.

Finally, where practical, try installing nesting boxes for birds, bats, hedgehogs, etc. The various wildlife charities will usually have such items for sale online if they are not available locally. Ensure that bird boxes are not placed in full sunlight: solar-roasted chicks is not really the purpose of installing them!

Questions to ask

- Do you use chemical pesticides?
- Are you using compost instead of artificial fertilizers?
- Do you use moss peat?
- Do you have an area set aside for wild flowers and plants?
- Do you provide bird or bat boxes?
- Do you have a pond?
- Do you have an area where old timber can rot?
- Have you reduced the area of manicured lawn to a minimum?
- Is the garden covered with concrete, gravel or decking?

Tips to encourage wildlife to your garden

1 Stop dead-heading all your flowers, as they are food for local birds.

2 Install a wildlife pond.

3 Install bird-feeders and water tables.

4 Put in bird and bat boxes.

5 Replace some of the grass lawn with a wild-flower meadow and allow some of the rest of the grass to grow uncut for a season.

6 Allow sections of the garden to grow wild.

7 Create an area where fallen branches can rot.

8 Allow ivy to take over garden walls.

9 Put a Catwatch on your cat to stop it killing birds (available from RSPB website).

10 Rip out any decking, gravel or concrete and allow nature back in.

Planting for wildlife

■ Holly is loved by thrushes, robins and finches.

■ Roses are great for bees and butterflies.

■ Ivy provides food for insects and birds such as tree-creepers and goldcrests.

■ Buddleia is good for hoverflies, butterflies and bees.

■ Honeysuckle attracts moths at night.

■ Red-berried pyracantha provides loads of food for birds in late autumn.

■ Uncut grasses provide seeds that birds love.

■ Sedum provides lots of nectar if planted in sunny, well-drained soil, so low-growing varieties are a favourite for roof gardens.

■ Lavender is liked by goldfinches and bumblebees.

For a comprehensive list go to the RSPB website and look under 'feed the birds'.

Tips for an eco-friendly garden

1 Do not use moss peat.

2 Do not use chemical pesticides and herbicides.

3 Create a compost heap for garden and home compost.

4 **If possible only water with rainwater from water butts.**

5 **Plant fruit trees and shrubs to reduce food miles.**

6 **Mix in vegetables and herbs with the flowering plants.**

7 **Grow your own plants from seeds.**

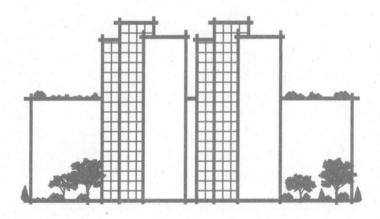

Work eco-audit

Nature may seem an odd thing to include in a workplace eco-audit, but business premises often have substantial grounds surrounding them that could be turned into a valuable resource.

Even if they only have a car park, planting trees there can absorb carbon dioxide and shade the cars in summer, so they do not overheat and require more air conditioning on the drive home. Planting deciduous trees at the south-facing aspect of an office block can help reduce solar gain in summer, thus helping to reduce the need for air conditioning, while allowing it in during winter. The same is true for exposed buildings: for example, planting evergreen trees to protect from the prevailing winds can help keep the exposed business premises warmer in winter.

Turning manicured corporate lawns into wildlife shrubberies and wild-flower meadows will not only reduce maintenance costs but also significantly increase resources for local wildlife. In addition, many premises may be situated beside waterways, such as canals, rivers or lakes. When I eco-audited NCVO, the UK national umbrella body for voluntary organizations, I was delighted to find they were protecting wild-fowl nesting sites where their inner-London premises faced an old canal. Such actions are not only good in themselves but can also provide immense pleasure to staff.

Even if the premises have no grounds, window boxes can be maintained and, as I mentioned above, bird-feeders and boxes can be placed on almost any building. Before positioning any such boxes, take advice from a charity such as the RSPB.

If there are grounds, you will need to find out if they are maintained by contractors or in-house staff. If the latter, have a chat with the people responsible to find out about whether they are using organic maintenance practices and wildlife-supportive practices. If the former, find out what their policies are about these issues and ensure that they are taken into account in any future tendering for grounds maintenance contracts.

All the other tips for home wildlife gardening will apply to corporate grounds, so just ensure that they are covered in the work nature eco-audit walkabout.

Questions to ask

- Does their in-house gardener or grounds maintenance staff have training in eco-friendly maintenance systems?
- Do they have a policy excluding the use of chemical pesticides and herbicides?
- Do they have a policy to encourage wildlife and wild flowers on the site?
- Do they have a policy excluding the use of moss peat?
- Do they have the space to plant more trees?
- Do they have or could they install a wildlife pond?
- Do they provide bird-feeders or a water table?
- Do they already have or could they place bird or bat boxes on the premises?
- Do they have or could they place window boxes on the window sills?

Chapter 6

Cleaning and maintenance

How to avoid taking the planet to the cleaners

Some household clients will be unfamiliar with the health and environmental consequences of many everyday cleaning and maintenance products. The problem is that they pollute our waterways and so damage nature. In addition, they consume vast quantities of oil in their production and transport, worsening global warming. The store of toxic cleaning chemicals under our sinks is the greatest source of accidental childhood poisonings.

Since 1945 over 72,000 synthetic chemical compounds have been developed, many of which have already been found to be toxic for humans, although only 2 per cent of these have been independently tested so far. Researchers in the USA found 167 artificial chemical residues within the human body when they tested volunteers. Of these, 76 caused cancers, 79 caused birth defects and 94 were toxic to the nervous system, with some contributing to more than one disease. Cosmetic and skin products are a particular problem, as many of the chemicals they contain are absorbed directly through the skin. The toxic components of lip products can, in addition to being absorbed, be directly swallowed. Campaigners have only partially succeeded in getting a ban on the inclusion of toxic phthalates in cosmetics. Many of the solvents used in nail products are also carcinogenic and are lung irritants.

After a long struggle with the powerful chemical industry, the EU is beginning to tackle some of this backlog, but it will never be able to test the millions of permutations and combinations that result from the mixing of such a huge list of artificial chemicals now present in our homes and workplaces. It is worth remembering that on average we now spend up to 90 per cent of our time indoors, whether at home or at work, so it is crucial from a human health point of view that the air indoors contains as few polluting chemicals as possible.

Those long supermarket aisles packed with hundreds of different plastic-packed chemicals represent another aspect of our destructive consumerism. The companies selling these mostly unnecessary products have also persuaded millions to buy one-use, throw-away items such as paper handkerchiefs, anti-bacterial surface wipes, one-use disposable dental floss applicators, kitchen towels, disposable razor blades, etc. But the good news is that you can have a beautifully clean and hygienic home without all these chemicals and also reduce the carbon footprint for cleaning your home.

Eco-friendly maintenance

As well as eco-cleaning, it is also important to ensure that any maintenance work done on a property is eco-friendly. Up to a third of the lifetime energy use of a building can be taken up in the manufacture of the materials that go into building it, such as bricks and steel girders. In addition, many of the paints and other compounds used in modern building methods contain an extraordinary range of toxic chemicals, many of which will continue leaking into the property's atmosphere long after the builders have left, and they also generate an enormous toxic waste mountain in their production. Moreover, building work on a property usually results in huge amounts of rubble and waste that has to be dumped in a landfill site. In the UK construction and mining waste makes up over half our total annual waste stream. This is fives times the domestic waste from all our homes put together, so it is really important to tackle the problem. An average house refurbishment can produce more unrecyclable waste than the domestic waste from a family for an entire year.

As the waste from a refurbishment is often really difficult to recycle, the most important thing is to avoid creating it in the first place and so, when eco-auditing homes, I often find myself looking into whether radical refurbishment or extensions are really necessary. A useful approach is to ask people why they are carrying out the building work and then see if there is a different way of using the existing building that would fulfil the same purpose.

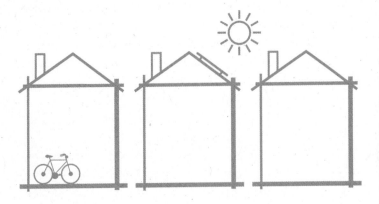

Home eco-audit

Kitchen

Underneath the sink is the usual place to start looking on this section of the walkabout, as this is where most people keep their cleaning products. If yours is an average house, this area is likely to be packed with all sorts of red and yellow plastic bottles shouting their claims to be the best and newest product for whatever niche piece of cleaning they specialize in. The plain fact is that the vast majority of these chemical-based cleaners are simply not necessary and there is nearly always a natural product that will do the job just as well, more often than not more cheaply and without the risk inherent in the use and storage of toxic chemicals in the home. Check that the washing-machine powder is not packed full of phosphates and chemical perfumes. Hopefully, having agreed to an eco-audit, people will realize that it is really important to only use the washing machine and dishwasher when they are full. That said, I have a friend who actually used his washing machine and drier to clean a favourite pair of socks he wanted to go out in...

One of the really difficult questions clients may ask you at this point is, if they decide there and then to stop using all of these horrible chemical concoctions, what should they do with the mountain of them they have already. Should they dump them in the bin, and so poison whatever landfill they end up in, or should they just continue using them until they are finished? My usual response, and this is what I did with some cleansing products left behind by former housemates, is to give them to somebody you know who does not care about environmental issues yet. At least this way it means they buy less of the stuff and you can start straight away with eco-cleaning.

While in the kitchen, do not forget to check whether people are using disposable wipes for surface and floor cleaning and paper kitchen towels. All of these are unnecessary consumables and are easily replaced with various kinds of reusable kitchen and floor cloths. A useful tip is to tell them about E-cloths, which do a great job of cleaning sinks and kitchen surfaces without the need for any scouring powder whatsoever. There is also a good E-cloth that cleans windows and mirrors without the need for any cleaning agent other than a little water.

If you have time and are specifically asked, quickly go through the various natural alternative cleaning products that people can use. The core of any natural cleaning approach is humble sodium bicarbonate, which is really effective in a whole range of situations in the home. Despite being an excellent oven and floor cleaner, it is safe enough to be taken as a remedy for indigestion, which of course means it is a whole lot safer to have around the home than most branded cleaners, with their phosphates, enzymes, artificial brighteners and toxic poison warning (see the list on pages 139–40 for details of natural cleaning tips). Soda crystals (sodium carbonate) are a coarser version of sodium bicarbonate and can be bought in large bags at many stores. They are excellent for a host of cleaning jobs around the house, such as floor and oven cleaning and drain clearing. I recently had bad odours emanating from my drains and feared something was broken down there, but after a few rounds of pouring soda crystals and hot water (rainwater heated on the wood-burner; three cups of soda crystals with about 8 litres of hot water) down the bath plughole a smell-free bathroom was thankfully restored!

Utility room

Once you have done the kitchen, your next port of call will probably be the utility room, if the house has one. Have a quick look at what dishwasher and washing machine powders are being used; if it is not natural products such as Bio-D or Ecover, make a note to investigate where they can be bought locally or online. For years I have been happily using Bio-D washing-machine liquid detergent, which is made from natural materials. Some eco-friendly shops even provide a refill service for such products, thus eliminating the packaging footprint. Instead of using an artificial fabric freshener, you could place lavender beads in the finished laundry instead, and suggest undiluted white vinegar for removing under-arm stains if you come across a bottle of bleach stashed away.

Bathroom

What no advertising campaign will tell you, because it does not sell products, is that the most important thing with cleaning is to give any surfaces that get grimy, such as the bathtub, toilet bowl and sink, a quick 30-second rub or brush every day. This will slash the need to use cleaning products there in the first place, as even natural products have an accompanying footprint for production, packaging and transport, etc., and you will certainly never need to use bottles of toxic bleach or nasty chemical-based cream cleaners. As for limescale, if the shower heads block up quickly because your home is located in a hard-water area, just apply a cloth soaked in white vinegar and that should clear them.

Check to see what sink and toilet cleaners are being used, and also what personal cleaning products, including shampoo, toothpaste and soap. Natural, chemical-free alternatives are available for all of these. Some companies produce solid shampoo soap bars that come in a paper bag and so dispose with the need for bottled shampoos. Bottled 'soaps' are not soap at all but an extraordinary concoction of chemicals. In addition, many of them contain anti-bacterial agents such as triclosan. Triclosan is a chlorinated, organic anti-bacterial chemical, traces of which have been found in fish and human breast tissue.

As well as being of environmental concern, this is also a general medical health issue. Anti-bacterial agents are crucial in hospital and clinical situations to ward off infections, but an increasing number of bacteria are gaining immunity to such agents. Their wholesale, indiscriminate use in homes and offices is an appalling waste of a vital tool in the fight against disease. It makes no sense to lose the effectiveness of such powerful anti-bacterial agents in return for millions of pointless disposable anti-bacterial floor wipes, counter wipes and bottled chemical 'soaps'.

Many European governments have already called for the public to avoid using household anti-bacterial products, which bring with them the additional problem of the disposal of millions of plastic bottles for packaging. The suggestion is that they replace such bottled 'soaps' with genuine vegetable-oil (avoiding palm oil, which drives rainforest destruction) soaps. If you are worried about such soaps making a mess on the sink, get a magnetic soap holder, which will keep the sink clean and also stop the soap dissolving in water. It is worth mentioning again that a quick swish of the sink daily with a nailbrush and the loo with the toilet brush will reduce the need for any other cleaning substances.

Some people have nasty artificial air fresheners stashed in the bathroom. If you come across these, suggest replacing them with pot-pourri instead. This is basically a collection of dried aromatic plants and can be refreshed, when the natural aromas have gone, by soaking in a plastic bag with some natural flower oils. While this, like all air fresheners, will mask any smells, bicarbonate of soda in a dish will actually absorb and remove the bad odours. However, the best method for removing smells is, of course, plenty of fresh air. There may be some shower curtain chemical fungicide lurking in the bathroom. Tea tree oil diluted in water will do the trick here.

Cosmetics can sometimes be stored in the bathroom, though they are more often stored in the bedroom. If you come across them, it will remind you to mention that there is now a wide range of natural cosmetics on the market. These avoid synthetic chemicals and many of them use only organically grown materials. They can be bought via the web, if they are not available in local health food stores.

Dry-cleaning

Before completing the indoor section, you need to think about dry-cleaning. The traditional chemical used is called perchloroethylene, which is a CFC and so contributes to the creation of the ozone hole in the atmosphere. It also causes kidney and liver damage to humans after repeated exposure. Ideally, you should avoid buying clothes that need dry-cleaning, but if you have such clothes already, seek out dry-cleaners who do not use perchloroethylene. These are slowly becoming more common. Perchloroethylene is also found in carpet and upholstery cleaners, so make sure you avoid their use in the home.

Outdoors

The remaining place on the walkabout that has relevance to cleaning and maintenance will be the garden shed, where paints are stored. One of the key things to look for here is whether the paints contain high levels of volatile organic compounds (VOCs). Some paints, especially high gloss varieties, contain up to 50 per cent VOCs, but even emulsion paints, which are largely water-based, can also contain low to medium levels. Research suggests that some VOCs cause chronic and acute health effects at high concentrations, and some are known carcinogens. Low to moderate levels of VOCs can also produce acute reactions. Manufacturers are now required to put a notice on paint tins informing users about VOC levels.

The problem with VOCs is at its worst at the time of painting, when the solvents evaporate into the air, creating a major health risk for the person painting and those in the room at the same time or soon after. However, they continue to leach into the air for years after and are a key contributor to so-called sick building syndrome. Reading the VOC labelling on paint tins can be a shock. Many people are completely unaware that it is there as a health warning. The good news is that there are now ranges of organic paints which are 100 per cent VOC-free. They are made mainly from plant and natural materials, rather than the petrochemicals used in mainstream paints. The slightly bad news is that they are up to three times more expensive. But as the purchase of paint is only an occasional occurrence for the average home, for the health of not only the household but also the painters it is worth making the extra investment. The gloss versions also take longer to dry, which can be an issue in some business situations. Natural organic paintbrush cleaners, thinners, wood stains and turpentine are also available.

Finally, check to see if there are any petroleum-based hand cleaners in the shed and, if there are, suggest a natural alternative, such as those made from hemp. In wealthier homes it is often not the householder who does the cleaning and decorating, so one of the recommendations will be for the relevant information to be passed on to the house cleaner, handy-person or decorators.

Questions to ask

- Do you use eco-friendly washing-up liquid, washing-machine and dishwasher detergents?
- Do you use non-toxic cosmetics?
- Do you use natural shampoos and sun-care products?
- Do you use non-toxic household cleaning products, such as bath, toilet, sink and oven cleaners?
- Do you use non-toxic air fresheners?
- Do you use natural furniture polishes and window cleaners?
- Do you use non-toxic paints and turpentine?
- Do you use anti-bacterial chemical-based bottled 'soaps'?
- Do you know about simple, traditional, natural, non-toxic, non-branded household cleaning materials, such as soda crystals, lemon, vinegar, borax and lavender?
- Do you reduce the need for cleaning materials in the first place by giving surfaces a regular wipe or brush?

Refurbishments and extensions

Sometimes during a walkabout, people will mention that they are thinking about refurbishing their house or planning an extension and ask for advice on the best eco-options.

Such work will have significant carbon dioxide, natural resource and waste implications, so the first and most important thing to talk through is whether it is actually necessary. On a number of eco-audits I have carried out, clients have decided, after talking the matter over, that on balance their extension was not needed after all.

For example, on one occasion in a very large house in south-west London my client was planning a major restructuring and extension of the ground floor, despite already having a very large sitting room, a nice conservatory and a more than adequate kitchen. When we discussed the benefits of the proposed restructuring, she admitted that actually there was very little; in fact, she realized that just because so many other people on the street had had similar work done she was subconsciously assuming she ought to as well! I think that two-minute conversation covered my fee nearly twenty-fold!

Another client, who lived in large converted stables in Oxfordshire, was planning a major extension and conversion of the garage areas adjacent to the kitchen. During the walkabout, I noticed that the room beside the kitchen was used as a dining room, while the living area was at the far end of the house. I suggested that they make the room beside the kitchen a living room instead, with a cosy wood-burner, and open it out to the garden by installing a bigger window. This would have the same effect as the proposed extension at a fraction of the environmental cost. They had not thought of this as an option, which incidentally would save them a considerable amount of money into the bargain.

One detail worth mentioning, if people are buying a new bathroom suite, is to suggest they get a coloured suite instead of white, thus removing the pressure for it to be always whiter than white. It is also worth asking if they are intending to do any chemical-based damp-proofing. If they are, suggest they look at natural methods, such as the Dutch Schrijver System, which uses natural ventilation to remove the damp and can be applied to nearly all existing housing, as well as new-build.

If, after discussion, it is clear that the refurbishment or extension is needed, or the client wants to go ahead anyway, it is important to recommend the use of architectural rescue building materials, which will eliminate most of the environmental footprint of new building materials. Building bricks for example use huge amounts of energy and CO_2 in their firing, as do steel girders and concrete. Thankfully the use of reclaimed products is now becoming fashionable. The Salvo website provides a list of architectural rescue salvage yards across the UK. Of course, if parts of the building are being demolished in preparation for the extension or renovation, it is important that as much of the existing materials as possible are reused. There are a number of issues to be considered:

• Can any of the existing building's materials – e.g. slates, tiles, wood, bricks, windows – be reused?

• Ensure that the maximum levels of insulation for floors, walls and roof spaces are installed.

• Can any architectural rescue materials – e.g. bathroom fittings, flooring, bricks – be used?

• Ensure that any new wood has Forest Stewardship Council (FSC) certification that it is legally and sustainably produced.

• Can any new products required be made from recycled materials – e.g. insulation made from recycled paper (Warmcel)?

• Ensure that no toxic paints, only organic ones, are used.

• Ensure that only the most energy-efficient electrical equipment is installed – e.g. AAA-rated kitchen white goods.

• Ensure that only the most energy-efficient lighting is installed, using the minimum number of light fittings necessary.

• Ensure that any water fittings are the most efficient on the market.

• Can any renewable-energy technologies be incorporated as part of the design – e.g. solar tiles instead of roof tiles if the extension is not overshadowed?

• Does the design take advantage of any potential for passive solar gain in winter and avoiding excessive solar gain in summer?

• Is a rain-harvesting system being installed?

Even counter tops for kitchens can now be made from recycled materials and a range of natural materials can be used in the building process, including hemp bricks, wooden beams instead of steel and lime wall renders. It is important to avoid the use of PVC for any guttering and drainpipes or for any new windows. Recommend metal guttering instead of PVC and wood frames for the windows, which now legally have to be at least double-glazed for all new buildings or extensions.

Tips for eco-cleaning at home

1 Use phosphate-free detergents for washing up and washing machines, such as those made by Bio-D and Ecover (phosphate-rich suds feed the algal blooms in our rivers and lakes, destroying wildlife).

2 Use environmentally friendly dishwasher gel detergent, which will also eliminate the excess packaging associated with many mainstream brands of dishwasher tablets. An even simpler alternative is to sprinkle bicarbonate of soda over the dishes before you turn on the machine.

3 Don't waste money on chemical-based window cleaners. Instead, use a spray gun filled with one part organic vinegar to four parts water. This will be just as effective but at a fraction of the price.

4 A lemon dipped in salt will replace nasty chemical brass cleaners, while scrubbing with sodium bicarbonate or wiping down with white vinegar will remove the limescale that builds up in hard-water areas.

5 Stop pouring bleach down your drains if you have a blockage. Instead, use a mix of boiling water, baking soda (bicarbonate of soda) and vinegar.

6 Use beeswax or carnauba polish on furniture instead of chemical-based products.

7 If there is ingrained dirt on your surfaces, use a solution of baking soda or the natural mineral borax and water to bring them up shiny and clean.

8 Use herbal toothpaste instead of a chemical-based one for a healthy mouth.

9 Use only organic shampoos and see if you can reduce the amount you use in the first place. Too much shampoo is bad for the hair.

10 Use natural bars of soap instead of plastic bottles of so-called 'anti-bacterial soaps', which are just a dreadful concoction of artificial chemicals.

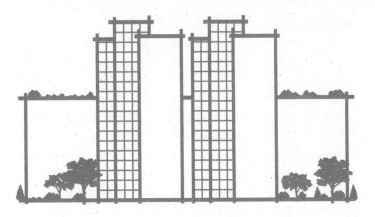

Work eco-audit

The first thing to do is to determine who exactly does the cleaning on the premises. This can vary from a named member of staff or in-house cleaner to an external cleaner employed directly by the company or a specialist cleaning company under contract to the company. The situation can be further complicated when you are working in shared premises, as the cleaning may not be the direct responsibility of the company being eco-audited; or in some cases, it will be carried out by the owners of the building or a building management company.

Once this has been established, you then need to find out who actually makes the decision on what cleaning products are purchased. In my experience, it can be anyone from the chief executive to the cleaners themselves. Obviously organizations differ in how they reach decisions, so it is your job as an eco-auditor to identify where the decision-making takes place. Once you have ascertained this, you know where to take your recommendations once you have completed your walkabout.

Canteen

Under the sink or in a nearby cupboard is usually a good place to start looking for information on cleaning issues. Just as in the average household, this is where many companies store their cleaning products. In my experience, company cleaners are far less likely than householders to be using eco-friendly products. They also use inordinately more really toxic chemicals. It is quite normal to come across huge stashes of undiluted bleach and scouring products, which get used far more profligately than most people would ever dream of at home, resulting in an often chemical fog in kitchens and toilets once the cleaners have finished.

For some bizarre reason, cleaners in commercial premises often seem to use litres of bleach. See if you can encourage them to cut back. Chemical-based limescale removers are another favourite. Applying cloths soaked in white vinegar to the affected areas is an effective natural method of getting rid of it.

Many companies approach cleaning products from a hard-nosed economic standpoint, with a mantra that emphasizes 'the bottom line'. This tends to result in the purchase of large amounts of the most toxic but cheapest, and so usually nastiest, cleaning products on the market. Suggest a reduction in the use of these chemicals and instead a return to daily manual cleaning, with chemicals to be used only when such manual cleaning does not work. No toilet needs daily bleaching, for example, and the use of sodium bicarbonate, which is cheaper than many branded cleaners, will also reduce costs, thus getting over any objections on that score.

Cleaners' storeroom

After checking under the kitchen sinks, you need to see if there is a cleaners' storeroom or cupboard. This is where you will be able to determine once again how eco-friendly current product practice is.

Determine for yourself whether recycled toilet paper and paper hand-towels are being used rather than taking anyone's word for it. I have found that people can make simple mistakes by misreading labels, but also that the situation can change from when they last checked on what was happening. For example, a cleaner who was originally buying recycled paper products might have moved on and the replacement might have different ideas. Interestingly, Tesco's cheapest brand of toilet paper uses recycled paper, as it should, because the raw material (waste paper) is readily available now that people have got into the habit of recycling. The supermarket decided not to clearly label it as such because surveys found that about 5 per cent of the UK public thought that recycled toilet paper was actually made from recycled toilet paper!

Having determined what types of products are being used by the cleaners, you will then, if necessary, have to persuade them to change to eco-friendly products. Who you need to approach will depend on the results of your earlier research into who makes the purchasing decisions. Sometimes you will come across companies that hire contract cleaners who claim they have environmental policies in place, but in my experience this often does not necessarily lead to environmental best practice. One approach is to suggest in your report that the next time the cleaning contract goes out to tender, the company should specify the use of eco-cleaning products and recycled paper. In addition, they could ask for cleaning staff to be trained to be environmentally responsible in how they go about their duties. Issues such as water efficiency, the use of chemicals and having lighting on only where necessary, need to be part of the cleaning regime, as they do in all other parts of a company's eco-performance. In many commercial buildings all the lights are left on during cleaning and, even worse, even when the cleaners have finished for the night, so they blaze away until the following morning. Dealing with this will require liaison between the company and the cleaning contractors.

Of course, if the cleaning is carried out in-house and you have the full backing of management, it should be easier to achieve change, as you will not have to deal with a remote management company or a large corporate cleaning company. On the other hand, if you were to manage to persuade a large cleaning contractor to clean up its act, then you would have helped them to become more eco-friendly in the other companies for which they clean. Never forget, though, that in many instances you will be asking employees who have been in place for years to radically change well-established and familiar work practices. Obviously you need to be sensitive to individual people's opinions, but it has been my experience that many cleaners are also enthusiastic about environmental issues and can be thrilled that an eco-audit is giving them management support to do their work in a more eco-friendly way.

Maintenance

On your walkabout, you may find there is someone responsible specifically for maintenance who also has a storeroom or cupboard. The key issues here are the kinds of paints and solvents being used and, if timber is bought in for repairs, whether it is certified by the Forest Stewardship Council.

Alarmingly, one serious problem I have come across while undertaking eco-audits is lack of knowledge about the dangers involved in using chemical-based paints, with their high VOC content. You will often find indoor maintenance workshops using such paints with very little ventilation. While this is a clear health and safety issue, it is useful to remind people in charge that the fumes from VOC paints are carcinogenic, so good ventilation is vital. Ideally, you should try to persuade people to switch to healthier and environmentally far more benign organic paints.

I had a friend staying for a while and he decided to paint his bedroom for me as a thank you. He had bought some high-VOC paint but I insisted that he could use only organic paint. When I came home the day he had finished, he greeted me by saying, 'I hate you!' with a large smile across his face. I asked why, and he explained that he liked the organic paint so much, he would never be able to use any other sort again, even though they are more expensive.

Demonstrating concern for staff by switching to organic paints could really boost morale and will also help to avoid sick building syndrome.

Questions to ask

- Is the cleaning done by an employee or a contract cleaning company?
- If the cleaning is done by an in-house cleaner, has anyone discussed with them cleaning in an eco-friendly way?
- If the cleaning is done by a contract cleaning company, has anyone asked about their environmental policy and for evidence of what action is being taken to implement it?
- Are eco-friendly cleaning products being used?
- Are non-toxic paints specified when estimates for redecoration are requested?
- If a window-cleaning company is used, are they asked to use natural window-cleaning materials such as vinegar?
- Are natural soap or bottled chemical anti-bacterial soaps used?

- If an in-house cleaner is used, is the company willing to take the time or spend the money to train them in eco-cleaning methods?

- If a contract cleaning company is used, would they be willing to incorporate eco-friendly products and working methods into their next tender, or even prior to that?

- Are the cloths assigned to various cleaning tasks reusable or does the company favour wasteful surface, floor and furniture anti-bacterial 'wipes' and paper towels?

- Is recycled paper used for products such as toilet paper, kitchen towels and serviettes?

- Where appropriate, are electric hand-driers used rather than wasteful paper hand-towels, which create a huge waste mountain? In certain clinical premises electric hand-driers are not favoured, but there are now low temperature models available that are suitable for use in such situations.

Chapter 7

Energy

Why saving energy matters

This chapter specifically covers energy saving in the home and in business premises; energy used for transport and holidays, as well as actually producing your own eco-energy from renewable sources, will be discussed later. The fact that the energy used in buildings in the UK makes up over 47 per cent of total UK carbon dioxide emissions is the best way to get across to people how important energy saving is for the environment. Nearly 25 per cent of UK emissions are from domestic homes – almost twice the amount from car use and over ten times more than from aviation refuelling. In other words, our homes are the biggest single source of emissions in the UK and hence a major contributor to climate chaos.

These UK building emissions contribute to total world carbon dioxide emissions, which in 2006 were 8 gigatonnes. Nature has always been able to deal with huge amounts of carbon dioxide. It is, after all, part of the natural carbon cycle, where plants absorb carbon dioxide and release oxygen, but nature's worldwide capacity to absorb the emitted carbon dioxide in 2006 was calculated at only 3.5 gigatonnes, which means a net increase of carbon dioxide in the atmosphere of 4.5 gigatonnes (a gigatonne is a billion tonnes!). In addition to the absorption of carbon dioxide by plants, the oceans are also huge absorbers from the atmosphere. However, some scientists have predicted that by the mid-21st century it will not be possible for nature to continue absorbing more and more carbon dioxide, which would mean that levels in the atmosphere start to climb faster. Alarmingly, in May 2007 results from research carried out in the Southern Ocean suggest that the amount of carbon dioxide being absorbed by the ocean has levelled out, meaning that its capacity has already been reached, over 40 years earlier than expected. To provide an example of the possible consequences of such enormous quantities of carbon dioxide emissions hitting the atmosphere, some scientists have warned that by 2040 the entire Arctic ice shelf could be gone in summer. As this global alarm bell has started to ring, cutting emissions by saving energy in our buildings is even more critical.

The good news, though, is that most existing buildings can cut their energy consumption, both by investing in increased efficiency and also by simply changing the way energy is used and so eliminating waste. The former approach involves a minimum to modest financial outlay, but will start paying back in cost savings very quickly; the latter actually costs nothing but involves some modest lifestyle changes and will start saving money immediately, as well as lowering emissions.

Types of energy used for heat in the home in the UK

The Department of the Environment has calculated the net carbon dioxide emissions for the different sources of heat used in domestic homes (see box below).

Comparing sources of heat

Source	Kg of CO_2 per kWh heat used
Wood	0.00
Mains gas	0.20
Bulk LPG (liquefied petroleum gas)	0.25
Heating oil	0.27
Coal	0.32
Smokeless fuel	0.40
Electricity	0.43

This makes it easy to see that anyone currently using mains electricity for heating could slash their emissions by over half if they switched to gas central heating, even without taking any other energy-efficient measures. The main reason for this is that large, central, fossil-fuel power stations are a very inefficient method of generating electricity, as up to 70 per cent of the energy is lost in heat at the power station itself and in transmitting the electricity down the power cables. So, unless you have an abundant source of renewable electricity, which is unlikely, you should favour gas in preference to electric heating, and the use of wood rather than coal if you have an open fire.

Is nuclear power the answer to global warming?

In my opinion, proposing nuclear power as the solution to our addiction to fossil fuels such as oil and gas is like proposing heroin as the solution to an alcohol addiction. However, a lot of my clients ask this question at some point during an eco-audit, so it is worth familiarizing yourself with the issues at stake here.

Time scale

The Stern Review states that we have only one decade to radically cut carbon dioxide emissions. It would be impossible to build a large enough number of nuclear power stations within that time to make any serious impression on total emissions.

Expense

The cost of nuclear power stations is such that they cannot be built without huge public subsidies and subsidized government insurance guarantees. In addition, the prices cited for nuclear electricity do not include clean-up costs. It has been estimated that the cost of cleaning up the UK's nuclear generating and military waste created up to 2006, plus long-term storage, would cost over

£160 billion. In other words, we are paying a huge price now for the cheap electricity people used in the 1960s and 1970s. It is not right that we should pass on even more prohibitive costs to the next generation.

Uranium supplies

According to the UK government's energy review, there is only enough available uranium to last 50 years. If we were to replace fossil fuels with uranium, it would run out significantly faster, leaving a huge problem by the middle of the century.

Waste

There is still nowhere to store the waste produced by nuclear power, despite the fact it has been in use for over half a century.

Danger

A major accident such as the one at Chernobyl in 1986 would make huge areas of the country uninhabitable. Moreover, nuclear installations are vulnerable to terrorist attack, unlike renewable energy installations.

Alternatives

There are less dangerous renewable alternatives. It takes only 660 large wind turbines to produce the same amount of energy as a nuclear power station.

In the light of these factors, it is obvious that the arguments for and against nuclear energy are a dangerous distraction from the bigger picture. While the current ageing nuclear power plants provide up to 20 per cent of UK electricity, that is only 3.5 per cent of total UK energy use. To eliminate UK carbon dioxide emissions would involve the building of over 250 new stations, at a huge cost and risk to future generations.

Committing to nuclear power would require long-term fixed-price contracts, reducing potential investment in renewables and energy efficiency, resulting in higher taxes and higher electricity costs, even though nuclear power is not carbon dioxide-free. Studies estimate that the carbon dioxide emitted during construction of plants and extraction and preparation of uranium is equivalent to a third of the emissions from fossil fuels.

Energy efficiency, changing lifestyles and installing renewable energy are far cheaper, safer, faster and more ethical ways to cut UK carbon dioxide emissions.

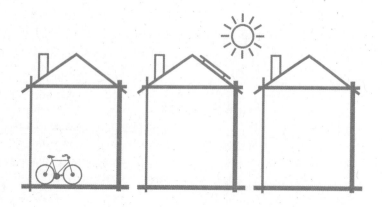

Home eco-audit

Energy use is one of the most important aspects of an eco-audit, so you will need to be very thorough in your walkabout. But before you even start, study the eco-audit form: the key figures here are the energy used for heating and electricity. If you find they are significantly above the average expected for the size of house or the number of people, you need to start looking for where energy is wasted.

For example, I was hired by a doctor's family in the Midlands and when I examined their form on the train journey there, I noticed that their electricity use was five times what I would have expected. Their gas use was about 20 per cent above the average, but that did not surprise me as they had a large home. The family did not seem to be extravagant and when I mentioned the very high electricity usage in our opening chat, they looked really perplexed. It soon emerged that the entire house was heated not by gas, which was used only for the gas Aga range and rarely for coal-effect gas fires, but instead by electric storage heaters, which were on full blast and gobbling energy. In addition, even though the gas figures initially looked normal, once my clients realized that they related not to the central heating but only the range and coal-effect fires, it became obvious how inefficient both of these products actually were.

Green electricity tariffs

It is important to know which company is supplying the electricity. Many people do not know what a green energy tariff is, so you must be able to tell them. Since the deregulation of the electricity market in the UK, customers have been able to choose who to buy their electricity from. Specialist green energy companies now sell eco-electricity made from renewable sources, such as wind, sun and water, to the national grid and you can buy it from them direct. You will obviously not be using the exact same electrons the green electricity company supplied to the national grid, but you will be buying the same amount from the grid as the company put in. Thus, at a stroke, all the carbon emissions from your electricity production can be eliminated without having to go to the expense of producing your own eco-electricity on-site.

However, this emphatically does not mean anyone should be wasteful with electricity. Buying green electricity helps to create a market, but the capital costs are still high and only a very small amount is as yet available. There is no way renewables will be able to supply all our currently wasteful lifestyles in the short term. However, if we really cut down on wasted energy, then they will be able to supply a greater proportion of our needs in a carbon-neutral way.

Like most things in life, some green electricity tariffs are better than others. Some are simply equivalent to a premium which the electricity company then uses to fund renewable energy projects but the energy they supply will not come from renewables themselves. Others are nothing more than a repackaging of their already existing hydroelectricity capacity. In a recent survey by the National Consumer Council, the green electricity supplier Good Energy was found to have the greenest electricity. Another supplier, Ecotricity, was found to have the highest investment in new capacity, while their entire electricity portfolio was not quite as green.

To switch to a green electricity company, all you need to do is get a copy of your electricity bill, fill in an application form online and then the company will contact your current supplier and sort out all the rest of the paperwork, or you can order the form by post. It really takes only a few minutes. There is about a 10 per cent premium for the greenest electricity, which works out at about £30 a year for the average home electricity bill – less than 60p a week or the equivalent of a fizzy drink!

Windows

These are one of the thinnest parts of the outer fabric of a building and a major source of heat loss. Note that anyone now replacing an entire window in the UK has by law to use at least a double-glazed unit. On your walkabout, have a careful look at every window, watching out for the following in particular.

Does the window close properly?

Many sash windows are broken, leaving a permanent gap which lets in a draught. If the catch is broken or missing on an outward-opening window, then it too might not close fully.

Recommendation: Ensure that any faults are repaired, so that all windows fit and draughts are excluded.

Is the window buckled or badly fitting?

Many metal-framed windows buckle over time and so become unclosable. Wooden windows can warp, letting in draughts.

Recommendation: Ideally you should get the windows refurbished so that they fit properly. However, if this is not within your budget, an interim option is to use strip insulation.

Is the window double-glazed?

Most older windows in UK homes will be single-glazed: i.e. they will not have a sealed vacuum or gas-filled double layer of glass.

Recommendations: If the window is strong and wooden-framed, it might be suitable for retro-fitting of a double-glazed unit. This means that the single pane of glass is taken out and replaced by a specially made double-glazed unit. There are companies who will come to your house and do the work on site. A cheaper option, if you are good at DIY, is to measure the window, order the unit and then install it yourself.

Either of these alternatives is far cheaper than the traditional approach to double glazing, which meant replacing the whole window, including the frame. Retro-fitting sash windows is a bit more difficult as the sash weights have to be adjusted to the heavier weight of the windows.

If the window is in a bad condition or you have a warped metal-framed window, then it probably is best to replace the frame also. Metal is a good conductor of heat and so is a bad material to use for windows.

If the window is not suitable for the retro-fitting of double-glazed units, another option is to consider secondary glazing. This means installing a separate pane of glass on a separate frame which is clipped onto the inside of the existing window. It needs to be well designed or some people may object on aesthetic grounds. Whilst a cheaper option than full replacement with double glazing, it is not as good in heat-retention terms but is a big improvement on a single-glazed window, especially if it is well sealed.

Is the window cracked?

As well as being dangerous, a cracked window will be the source of a draught.

Recommendation: Cracked windows should be fixed as soon as possible to eliminate the draught, but a short-term measure is to seal it up with tape.

Does the window have thermally lined curtains?

Having good-quality thermally lined curtains (also called inter-lining) for a window can help reduce heat loss through the glass and prevent draughts getting into the heated room.

Recommendation: Hang curtains at the windows that currently have none and get thermal lining for the poorly lined ones. Good-quality second-hand curtains are often freely available, for example on eBay and Freecycle. There is even a chain in the UK called The Curtain Exchange, which specializes in dealing in top quality reused curtains.

Doors

These are another large source of heat loss from the outer fabric of the building, so it is crucial on your walkabout that you examine all outer doors carefully, including any conservatory or front lobby doors. However, do not forget the inner doors, including those to unheated basements or cellars. People often forget that if a basement is open to the cold outside air, then the door leading from it into the main house is the equivalent of an outer door and so could be a major source of heat loss if not draught-proofed.

Does the door have a draught-proofed letter box?

A draughty letter box will be a large source of heat loss.

Recommendation: Ensure the letter box has draught-excluding brushes installed.

Does the door have keyholes that are sources of draughts?

Locks and keyholes are simply the equivalent of holes in an outside door. There should be regulations requiring all locks to be draught-proof.

Recommendation: If possible install a keyhole flap. If, due to the design of the lock, this is not possible, consider getting an architectural rescue lock to replace the current lock or place some tape over it if the lock isn't used.

Does the lock or catch on the door keep the door closed properly?

Old, defective locks or catches can result in doors not closing properly and so being very draughty.

Recommendation: Get the lock or catch adjusted to ensure the door closes properly.

Is there a gap under the bottom of the door?

It is amazing how often there is a large gap under many outside doors, allowing huge amounts of cold air into homes. As you actually have to get down on your hands and knees to see, this is often overlooked.

Recommendation: Install a door-brush to block the draught or, if necessary, install a wooden door lip if this is missing. Another option is to have a door draught-blocker, but these can be fiddly and people often forget to push them up against the base of the door.

Is there a gap at the side or top of the door?

If you can you see light or feel draughts along the edges or top of the door, you need to remedy the situation.

Recommendation: Install low-cost strip insulation.

Does the door itself have any gaps in it?

You will sometimes find the door itself may be broken or cracked, thus allowing cold air in.

Recommendation: Replace or repair the door so that it becomes air-tight again.

Is there a door curtain in place?

Door curtains were quite popular in Victorian times, for the very good reason that they kept out draughts.

Recommendations: If you can afford it, install a thermally lined door curtain that is weighted at its bottom. This will make the hall or room inside the outside door cosier. If there is no space at the side of the door for the curtain when it is pulled back, you can extend the curtain track along the adjacent wall.

If cost is an issue, cheaper items such as keyhole flaps, letter boxes and strip insulation are a higher priority. A door curtain is at the luxury end of recommendations.

Fireplaces

After windows and doors, fireplaces are the most common source of draughts in rooms. People tend not to pay too much attention to their fireplaces, so do not realize that these are effectively large holes in the middle of their house, letting out warm, centrally heated air. While fireplaces are most common in living or dining rooms, keep an eye out for them in other rooms, as unused fireplaces can often be found hiding behind furniture or piles of junk.

What fuel is being used?

Smokeless coal used in urban smoke-free zones has the highest carbon dioxide emissions of any solid fuel. Coal is also very high, but wood is carbon neutral. That said, burning wood in an open fire is four to five times less efficient than using a wood-burning stove.

Recommendation: At the very least, switch from coal to wood. Ideally, install a wood-burning stove, if wood is available locally (see pages 200–203 for more details).

Are all unused fireplaces sealed up?

Up to 20 per cent of heat can be lost through an unused fireplace if it is still open to the outside.

Recommendation: Seal up unused fireplaces or, if they are very rarely used, install a chimney balloon, which will cost about £20. These are made of industrial plastic and are easily blown up upon installation. They seal off over 99 per cent of the airflow and dissolve if a fire is lit accidentally without taking it out. They are not really suitable if the fire is used regularly.

Does the fireplace have a coal-effect or traditional radiant gas fire?

Coal-effect gas fires are scandalously wasteful compared to other gas fires and central heating systems. They are between 10 and 20 per cent efficient, depending on their age and model, which means that the vast majority of their energy is wasted up the chimney. Most of the gas used is merely for aesthetic effect, which is totally unacceptable in the light of the climate crisis. In addition, even when the gas fire is not running, the fireplace is losing heat if the room is centrally heated, because of the open flue going up the chimney.

Recommendations: Suggest that the coal-effect gas fire is never used if at all possible and that the chimney is sealed with a chimney balloon. On no account seal up the chimney in any other way with a coal-effect fire in place, as this is illegal and a serious health hazard.

Alternatively suggest replacement with a traditional radiant gas fire, whose efficiency is over 60 per cent, or if practical with a flueless gas fire. Flueless gas fires achieve an extraordinary almost 100 per cent efficiency, as the integrated catalytic converter converts all the gas into CO_2, heat and condensation. The catch, however, is that they are suitable only for houses with background central heating, as the condensation can lead to considerable damp problems otherwise and they are not suitable for very small rooms. They are, however, compatible with wood-burning stoves if used occasionally. There is now a whole range of looks for such flueless gas fires, from traditional coal-effect to modern minimalist models.

Walls

Up to 50 per cent of the total heat lost from buildings is through the walls. When you are outside on your walkabout, check to see if the building is brick-built. If it was built after the 1920s, it is likely to have cavity walls, which means there are two layers of bricks with a gap between them. It is crucial that this gap is filled with insulation. This is done by drilling a hole in the wall and pumping in the insulation. It costs only about £150 for the average house and you will make the money back within one or two years. This means it is one of the most effective investments you can make. You can tell if a brick building is cavity-walled if every second brick is not a half-brick. Pre-1920s solid-walled brick houses used such half-bricks between every full brick. Note, however, that most post-1995 cavity-walled buildings will already have the cavity filled with insulation.

If yours is a solid-walled building, then it will be more expensive and difficult to deal with. To install wall insulation on the outside of a building can cost over £5,000 and it will take more than 25 years to see savings but it can be very effective. It can also seriously affect the look of the building. If you are redecorating an external wall and battened insulation has been ruled out, there is now an insulation material that, whilst not as effective, is better than nothing – it goes on like a wallpaper and can be decorated over. Internal battened wall insulation involves the loss of some living space and is quite an upheaval for the average household to go through if they are not already refurbishing that particular room, but it is very effective. However, it really should be considered when a house is undergoing major refurbishment, as it can save up to 25 per cent of the annual heating bill. A layer of cork will also provide some thermal insulation and as well as being a completely natural product, it can also be an interesting design element that may not need painting.

Roofs

It is tempting to avoid clambering up into the loft space when doing your walkabout but it really is essential to have a look if it is at all possible. You need to know not only how much loft insulation (if any) there is but also whether there are any major gaps that are letting draughts in. It is also useful to check if the insulation has been stripped away and if the holes left unsealed by anyone who was installing halogen bulbs. Even if there is insulation up there, it might only be very early-1980s standard. Modern regulations stipulate a minimum of 270 mm of insulation but the more you put in the better, as about a third of heat loss from the building will be via the roof. Installing loft insulation can cost as little as £140, with an incredibly short payback period of less than a year. Think how much you could save over ten years! There are often grants available, especially for pensioners and people on benefits.

Various different types of insulation materials are used in lofts. The most common, and that used in most grant schemes, is mineral wool. However, this has a high energy cost in its manufacture and is very irritating to the skin and lungs; masks must be worn when installing it. New versions that have a plastic wrapping protect those coming into contact with it but will slightly increase the embedded energy used.

A number of natural alternatives are available. These include Thermafleece, which is made from sheep's wool, and Warmcel, which is made from mineralized recycled paper, plus options made from flax. A study by the consumer magazine *Which?* found that Warmcel had the best insulation properties of all the products tested, as well as of course providing an excellent market for recycled paper. It is easily installed, but on the downside it is quite fluffy, so if the loft is being accessed frequently it will blow about and make a mess unless sealed in. It is excellent for insulating hard to access places, as it can also be blown in by special installers.

Lighting

Almost every room will have lighting of some sort and this is one of the easiest areas in which to cut wastage. In the UK, lighting accounts for 7 per cent of total electricity production and energy-saving bulbs use up to 80 per cent less electricity than traditional tungsten bulbs. So if everybody switched to energy-saving bulbs from the old-fashioned tungsten or halogen, we could save over 5 per cent of total electricity production. This would equate to being able to close four and a half nuclear power stations (not that

I'm sure you can close half a nuclear power station, but that's statistics for you!). Australia has recently announced a phase-out of tungsten bulbs and will save over 4 million tonnes of carbon dioxide by 2012 thanks to this one measure alone. A group of the UK's major retailers has agreed to do the same in the UK over the next four years. Worldwide lighting consumes about 20 per cent of total electricity production, which causes the release of over 1.9 billion tonnes of carbon dioxide, which is about three-quarters of what our cars belch out.

A very useful way of getting across to people how much energy they are potentially wasting is to note down the total wattage for lighting in each room as you do the walkabout. Simply add up the wattage for every bulb used in the room. Then in the eco-audit report tally up the total for the whole house. I find the average household that has not switched to energy-saving bulbs uses between 3,000 and 6,000 watts to light their homes. The highest I have come across to date was a home in Henley-upon-Thames, which used a whopping 13,000 watts for lighting, equivalent to four electric immersion heaters! In comparison, my two-bedroom house is lit by a total of 190 watts. The UK Lighting Federation estimates that UK households could cut their electricity bills by a third if they switched to energy-saving bulbs.

Energy-saving bulbs now come in a range of styles and to fit most requirements, including small, elegant candle bulbs. No longer are we stuck with the ugly, clunky versions that first came on the market some 15 years ago. Some people may object on the grounds that they do not like the quality of light obtained, but that is no excuse. Nowadays not only are there daylight energy-saving bulbs available, but the tone and yellowness of the light can always be adjusted, depending on the lampshade used, to replicate the old-fashioned tungsten bulbs people had become used to. There are even some energy-saving bulbs with the same round shape as the old tungsten bulbs.

Even better is the fact that energy-saving bulbs have fallen in price. Some supermarkets in the UK are now selling them for as little as 99p and you can get them as cheap as 75p on some internet sites. As the Energy Saving Trust says, replacing one bulb could save up to £9 worth of electricity a year, and as it will last up to ten times longer, over its ten-year life you could save up to £90! LED lamps last even longer, with an extraordinary lifespan that is up to 50 times greater than that of a tungsten lamp.

It is also important to check whether there are simply too many light fittings in a room. One of the things I always like on an eco-audit walkabout is when the client starts self-auditing after a couple of rooms, and, for example, announces before you do that there is no need for extra lights in a room and actually takes the bulbs out there and then!

Watts what?

The jargon around the amount of energy used by light bulbs can be confusing, so you will need to get the basics clear in your mind. In essence, bulbs have always been classified by the amount of energy they use, rather than the amount of light they give out, which would have made more sense. This came about because for years the tungsten bulb was the only sort widely available and so the energy used equated with the amount of light provided. The amount of electrical energy used by bulbs or electrical equipment is measured in watts. The amount of light emitted by a bulb is measured in lumens, but this measurement is almost never used by the public.

Energy-saving bulbs give out the same amount of light or lumens for far fewer watts thanks to more efficient compact fluorescent technology. They are simply miniature compact fluorescent lamps, like the sort you see in offices or warehouses but folded over on themselves. Old-fashioned tungsten bulbs were terribly inefficient because over 80 per cent of the electricity was being converted into heat instead of light. Making sure people understand bulb ratings is important, as many people dismiss energy-saving bulbs as not giving enough light, when the real problem is that they did not choose a bright enough bulb in the first place.

Energy-saving v. tungsten/halogen bulb consumption

- A 20-watt energy-saving bulb gives the same light as a traditional 100-watt bulb

- An 11-watt energy-saving bulb gives the same light as a traditional 60-watt bulb

- A 7-watt energy-saving bulb gives the same light as a traditional 40-watt bulb

---

Lighting myths

Some people think it is better to leave a light on to save energy, rather than turning it off and then on again later when required. This is a classic example of something that was true long ago but continues to do the anecdotal rounds. In the 1950s, when fluorescent tube lighting was first introduced, the attached little motor that powered the start-up used about half an hour's electricity. This still made sense for factories and offices, because once up and running they used far less energy than tungsten bulbs. Thus, if you were leaving a room for just a few minutes in the 1950s, you would have been better to leave such bulbs on. However, things have improved immensely since the 1950s and the start-up motor now uses less than 30 seconds' worth of electricity. So it always makes sense to turn the lights off when you have finished with them.

It can be very satisfying as an eco-auditor to lay that particular canard to rest!

The halogen plague

The plague that I am on about is the fashion to replace traditional lamps that hung in the centre of a room (sometimes called pendant lamps) with a plethora of so-called down-lighters. They are usually situated in a little metal tube sunk into the ceiling and have small, round bulbs with a flat head, which are halogen bulbs. There is a whole raft of reasons why they are a bad idea; from an environmentalist's point of view, they are a real nightmare, multiplying the amount of electricity needed to light a house. In other words, halogen fittings do the complete opposite of what you are aiming for. Whereas a house fitted with old-fashioned tungsten bulbs will use up to five times more energy than a house fitted with energy-saving bulbs, a house fitted with halogen bulbs can use up to 25 times more!

Why halogen-bulb fittings are bad

- The average halogen bulb uses 40–50 watts. This is five times more than an equivalent energy-saving bulb which uses 7 watts but provides the same amount of light.

- As they are usually used for down-lighters, this means that over 60 per cent of the light is lost in the tube, instead of lighting the room, so they only light the area immediately beneath them. Thus a lighting design using halogen-bulb down-lighters will usually require between five and ten times more bulbs and fittings.

- If a room has been converted to halogen lighting and is using, say, 20 halogen bulbs, these will produce about 1,000 watts' worth of heat as well as light. If the room is

---

air-conditioned, this means the air-conditioning has to deal with the equivalent of an electric fire as well as the external heat of the day, causing it to work even harder and waste even more energy.

- Many of the halogen fittings when put into top-floor ceilings are not sealed off properly and so in winter allow warm air to escape into the loft area and allow a cold draught down into the bedrooms below. Make sure you check for this when on the top floor of a house that has halogen bulbs.

- Because halogen bulbs produce large amounts of heat, you will often find that where they have been installed in top floors, the loft insulation material has been ripped away from around them to prevent the danger of fire, so you lose even more energy from wasted heat. You will find out if this has happened when doing the loft section of your walkabout.

Ideally, you should replace the halogen down-lighting system with pendant (hanging) and standard lamp alternatives, both of which can have energy-saving bulbs attached and will slash the number of bulbs needed for bright and ambient lighting.

If there are loads of halogen fittings in a room and you do not want to install pendant lamps or want to go to the expense of replacing the fittings, you could simply remove a number of the bulbs themselves.

It is possible to get energy-saving bulbs that can be used in halogen bulb GU 10 fittings. They are called CFL (compact fluorescent lamp) bulbs and they use about 7 watts to give the same light as a halogen bulb. As they are fairly new, they are still a bit expensive but they last up to ten times as long and use a fifth of the energy. There are now even CFLs that fit halogen fittings and are dimmable, but these are even more expensive.

There are now ultra-low LED lamps also on the market that can also be used in GU10 halogen-type fittings. They give off slightly bluish-white light, which you may not like, but they are extremely low energy users (1 or 2 watts) and are appropriate where the light does not have to have a pleasant ambience, such as sensor-controlled security lighting, bathrooms or lighting a small work desk at night.

If you do not want to replace halogen fittings in the top floor of the house, you should put in heat protector fittings above the bulbs in the loft to prevent fire and to ensure that the fitting is sealed to eliminate draughts. Then if the lighting installers have damaged the insulation around the fitting, it can be repaired.

Finally, Osram have brought out a halogen bulb that uses 30 per cent less energy and works in low voltage systems. While not as good as CFL or LED, at least it is a step in the right direction.

Up-lighters

Having got the message across that halogen down-lighters are something to be strongly disapproved of, you also need to keep an eye out for up-lighters, which can be even worse. Up-lighters usually come in two forms. They are often used in a free-standing lamp with a large metal bowl, from where they throw the light up to the ceiling rather than into the room. Because the design is so stupid, most of the light is actually lost in the metal bowl and so a very large-wattage bulb is necessary to compensate. Most of the bulbs I have come across in uplighters vary from 200 to 300 watts and they are usually of a special tube-like design. Even then, the resulting light actually getting back down to the room is only the equivalent of an 11-watt energy-saving bulb and so it is using about 20 times more energy than required. Sometimes up-lighters do take ordinary tungsten bulbs, which can then be swapped for energy-saving bulbs, but the best thing is replace them with a pendant lamp or ordinary standard lamps (preferably second-hand versions) that are fitted with energy-saving bulbs and do not waste the light by throwing it up to the ceiling rather than into the room where it is actually needed.

Heating controls: the BIG, BIG issue

Sorry to be a bit melodramatic but I really wanted to draw your attention to what is probably the most important part of not only the energy-saving section of the eco-audit but the entire eco-audit itself. For me, one of the great revelations of actually doing eco-audits in homes and businesses is how many people do not have a clue about how the heating controls on their central heating or hot-water systems actually work.

This is not surprising as most people inherit whatever heating system is already present when they buy a house and familiarizing themselves with instruction booklets is usually not at the top of people's minds when they are in the process of moving. A quick explanation by the previous owners (if indeed they knew how the systems worked themselves) may be the best most people get and usually they will be too shy to say they do not understand.

Many people simply press the override button and have the central heating on all day. I have come across others who leave their hot-water cylinders on 24 hours a day, just because it is simpler than trying to find out how the controls and timers worked. Plenty of people do not know how to locate, let alone control, the timers (if indeed there are any timers on the systems in the first place – there usually are) or even adjust the settings on the temperature/thermostat.

A central heating system uses 10 per cent more energy for every degree it is above 19°C. If you have the system permanently set at 26°C (and I have come across this more than once), you will be using 70 per cent more energy than a home with its thermostat set at 19°C. And as central heating can be the source of over two-thirds of household energy carbon dioxide emissions, it is impossible to over-emphasize the importance of this issue.

Hot water

Similarly, for hot-water systems you will find timers over-ridden and therefore on 24 hours a day. In addition you will find them set at temperatures of up to 90°C, thus wasting buckets of energy. The recommended temperature setting is 60°C.

By talking with the household about when they shower, you might be able to eliminate the need to have the system on both in the morning and evening by getting them to agree when to shower. In addition check that any hot-water tanks are professionally lagged to ensure that the precious hot-water heating is not wasted.

Radiators

It is important to have a good look at the radiators on your walkabout, as this is how the central heating boiler delivers heat in most homes. (If, however, you have underfloor heating, make sure the floors are not covered with carpet or suchlike.) In particular, watch out for the following.

Are radiators located on outside walls?

Ideally radiators should be placed on inside walls so that heat does not leak directly through an adjacent external wall to the outside. However, it is not usually practical to recommend that radiators on external walls be moved, unless you are planning major refurbishment, including installing or moving radiators. (Obviously, if you are refurbishing, do not move radiators to an outside wall.) Instead, fit reflector insulation panels throughout the house behind all radiators that are on outside walls. These are easily installed and will reflect the heat into the room rather than leaking it into wall behind it. Up to 30 per cent of a radiator's heat can be lost through the adjacent outside wall.

In rooms where you have radiators on both outside and inside walls, give preference to using the radiators on the inside walls if possible.

Are radiators under windows?

Radiators directly under windows can lose much of their heat through the glass above, especially if the window is not double-glazed. This can be corrected by installing a shelf above the radiator, with insulation attached underneath the shelf to direct the warm air from the radiator into the room.

Does the radiator have a thermostatic control valve (TCV)?

These allow temperatures to be controlled individually and are essential for economical use of central heating systems.

Are the TCVs in working order?

They should be maintained as part of any annual boiler maintenance contract. You would be amazed at the number of homes that have had broken radiator controls for years prior to an eco-audit visit.

Are radiators blocked by furniture?

Many radiators are obscured by sofas or desks, ensuring that more of their heat is lost.

Are there any vents or holes to the outside behind the radiators?

It does happen. In one north London home I eco-audited, all the ground-floor radiators for some inexplicable reason had large air vents placed directly behind the radiators on the outside walls, leading to even more heat loss.

Are radiators obscured when curtains are drawn?

While I would normally recommend that heavy-duty, thermally lined curtains are installed to retain heat within a home, if they obscure a radiator placed under a window they will do the opposite of what is required. If a radiator has been unfortunately placed under a window, then the curtains need to be cut, so they do not stop the heat from spreading into the room. You can increase the curtains' effectiveness by placing Velcro along the edges so that the windows can be sealed off at night.

Electronics

Households these days have a huge number of electronic gadgets compared with even 20 years ago. Everything from PlayStations to laptops are now common in most homes. This has lead to a 40 per cent rise in electricity use for electronic goods in the home, with another massive 80 per cent rise predicted over the next five years. Ensure as you do your walkabout that these items are not left on, left on stand-by or left charging when the item has been removed. Even if something is switched off, it may be still pulling electricity from the mains. If you have a plug-in energy tracker, this will tell you. On one eco-audit I did, I found that even though the TV was turned off and was not on stand-by, it was still pulling about 60 watts from the mains and so needed to be turned off at the plug.

The Energy Saving Trust estimates that in the UK over 480,000 tonnes of carbon dioxide are emitted each year by TVs on stand-by. In addition, many mobile phone chargers that are not turned off at the plug when the phone is removed, use about 5 watts continuously. If the black adaptors on turned-off electronic gadgets are warm that tells you that they are wasting electricity.

Keep an eye out as you do the walkabout for any extractor or ventilation fans. Balancing excellent insulation with adequate ventilation is one of the most difficult things to achieve in an energy-efficient house. Traditional extractor fans waste large amounts of energy as they remove the heat as well as the stale air and the moisture that contributes to condensation. They waste about a million kilowatts of energy in the UK alone. There are now clever heat-recovery ventilators that capture the heat from the outgoing air and heat the incoming air with it. These can capture up to 73 per cent of the wasted heat and could slash that million kilowatts by half. Companies such as Ventaxia or Kair Ventilation provide a range of heat-exchange extractors if one is necessary. Personally, I prefer to open the windows and doors for half an hour to allow fresh air in. The best time to do this in winter is just before you are about to go out, as you will not then be wasting any heat. As there is a legal requirement to have ventilation in windowless toilets, it is better to avoid placing toilets in rooms without windows rather than installing an extractor fan.

Electric towel rails!!!

The exclamation marks are there for a reason. I have on a number of occasions been hired to do an eco-audit by environmentally conscious householders who were also concerned about the size of their electricity bills. It turned out that they had old electric towel rails in their bathrooms, which they left on all year round, 24 hours a day. You only have to do a quick calculation to work out that an 800-watt electric towel rail x 24 hours per day x 365 days per year = 7,008,000 watt hours = 7,008 kWh @11p per unit = £770.88!

One client, an elderly widow, had two towel rails on all year. Another time, I came across about ten towel rails spread right through a building that I was eco-auditing prior to the new owner moving in; I never saw the actual electricity bill but dread to think how many tonnes of carbon dioxide a year they were spewing out. Modern electric towel rails use about 300 watts, but the emissions and cost calculations are still prohibitive. The extraordinary thing is that, even if you do feel a warm towel is essential to your well-being, electric towel rails are more often than not completely unnecessary. You can put your towel over a radiator, in an airing cupboard or on a rack next to a radiator. The effect will be the same, but at zero extra energy cost.

The recommendation really has to be, if possible, get rid of these environmental monsters – but be diplomatic in your use of language!

Energy ratings

When you are buying new electronic equipment, whether it is a fridge or a television, it is crucial to check the energy rating or consumption. Remembering that 'A++' or 'Green' is the most energy-efficient, you should only be buying A++- or Green-rated products. This is because, once bought, that is the amount of energy it will consume every time it is used for the rest of its life. For example, an A-rated fridge will use up to 60 per cent less electricity than a G-rated fridge, which is a big saving, especially when you take into account that a fridge is one of the few electronic items in a home that is on 24 hours a day, all year round. The Energy Saving Trust estimates that buying an energy-efficient fridge-freezer can save £450 over ten years. An A+ fridge will use 25 per cent less energy that a simple A-rated fridge.

While on the subject of fridges, on your walkabout keep an eye out for how the fridges are being used. About a quarter of the houses I have eco-audited to date have had more than one fridge or freezer lying over half empty. By simply rationalizing how they stored their cooled food, they were often able to turn one off after my visit. Another frequent issue with fridges concerns the new fashion for refrigerated drinks cabinets, which will often have only a couple of cans of beer and a few bottles of wine in them. These can easily be moved into the fridge and the cabinet turned off completely. If not, at least turn off the display lighting in the cabinet, which is not necessary 95 per cent of the time and is adding to the temperature in the cabinet for no good reason.

Having checked the energy rating of the washing machine, it is important to remember that coloureds can usually be effectively washed at 30°C, rather than 60°C. This will save more than 50 per cent of the energy used every time clothes are washed at this temperature.

If you have a drier, you should really think about the detrimental effect this is having on the planet. Driers use over 4 kWh of electricity per cycle and clothes can often be dried equally effectively outside, if you have access to a garden, in summer or beside a radiator on a clothes horse in winter. What's more, clothes last longer if dried naturally.

Security lighting

Keep an eye out for external security lighting when doing your walkabout around the outside of the house. You will often come across systems that not only use very high-wattage floodlighting but are also on all night (on occasions I have actually come across such lighting on 24 hours a day!). This is both appallingly wasteful and means that the lighting is not doing the job required to make the house safer. If the lights are on all through the night, it means that when any intruder approaches the house there is no change in lighting to alert either the householders or their neighbours that something is amiss.

The answer is to install movement and light sensors in the security-light system, so that the lights only come on when an intruder approaches after dark. This low-cost simple measure will cut down the waste in security lighting by up to 99 per cent, without even changing the bulbs.

Ideally, if floodlighting or high-wattage lamps are being used, they should be replaced with energy-saving lamps. Solar-powered sensor security lighting is now on the market, although the range available as yet is not enormous.

Greenhouse

The final part of your walkabout will cover the garden, where there may be a greenhouse that is artificially heated in winter. Dick Strawbridge has an ingenious method of heating a greenhouse naturally by storing the heat of the sun in broken glass beneath the greenhouse floor. Full details can be found in his excellent book *It's Not Easy Being Green*.

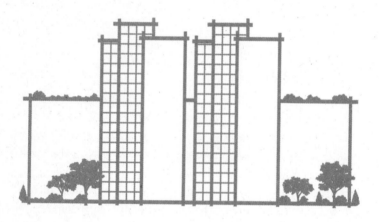

Work eco-audit

The eco-audit form will have told you what forms of energy are being used by the organization, so one of the first places to go in your walkabout is the plant room or wherever the central heating and hot-water boilers are located.

Boilers

The usual forms of energy used are oil, gas and electricity. With gas boilers it is important to find out the age of the boiler; modern condensing gas boilers use up to 36 per cent less energy than old heavy boilers. Old electrical heating systems can be far worse. The Royal Institute of British Architects recently replaced theirs with a new gas condensing boiler and cut emissions by 70 per cent. The excellent Boiler Efficiency Database compares the various types of boilers, including gas, oil and LPG. Boilers which used to be only about 55 per cent efficient – in other words, only about 55 per cent of the fuel got converted into usable energy – are now hitting extraordinarily high efficiency ratings of above 90 per cent. The most efficient gas combination condensing boiler listed currently is the Glow Worm Ultrapower 170SXI, which is floor-mounted. Oil and LPG can hit even slightly higher efficiencies. It is important, therefore, to recommend that if a boiler was installed pre-1995 the company should very seriously investigate its performance and seriously consider the cost and environmental benefits of installing a newer, more efficient system.

Having looked at the age issue, the controls are the next important thing to consider. As we have already seen, these can be a major source of energy loss on two counts: often the employees who were present when the system was installed have moved on, without imparting their working knowledge of the controls, and the instruction manual is almost bound to be missing. Even if this is not the case, you will need to go through in some detail the timings of both the hot-water and central heating systems, to ensure that they are in line with the work requirements. Ideally, if the building is well insulated, the central heating should only come on about half an hour prior to the first person arriving at work.

Again depending on insulation levels, it should be possible for the system to be turned off after a couple of hours once the building is warmed up, with maybe a boost in the middle of the day if necessary. The system should be turned off about an hour prior to the last person finishing work. Requirements will obviously vary from business to business, according to individual work patterns, the state of the building and the nature of the work involved. The other crucial question to ask when dealing with central heating controls is how the temperature is set. You need to ascertain if there is a central thermostat and if so what temperature it is set at, and if it and the individual radiator controls are included in an annual maintenance regime for the boiler. You would be amazed how many organizations that pay for their boiler to be maintained have broken thermostats and radiator valves. The recommended temperature setting for an office is 19°C.

The same amount of attention needs to be paid to the hot-water system. This can be a separate system or integrated into the central heating system. Even if integrated, it is still important to go through the timings. If the instruction manual has been lost or employees do not know how to operate them, you will sometimes find that the override switch has been used and the hot water can be on 24 hours a day. Many office buildings will not need much hot water, other than a small amount for the bathroom sinks or the odd bowl of washing up, especially if there are no showers being used on site. However, hot-water timers are often set to come on with the central heating, resulting in far too much being produced; it is also common to find that the hot water is kept on for very long hours in summer, when the central heating is off. That said, in a number of companies I have found that the central heating boiler is left on right through the summer, to the astonishment of the management when I point it out. So, it is often possible to cut down the central heating hours radically. The main thing is to encourage the organization to experiment with the timers to find out how little they can use while still maintaining the necessary space heating and hot water needed for staff.

Just as in the domestic eco-audit, it is really important to check the hot-water temperature, which if set too high will waste significant amounts of energy. The recommended setting is 60°C, because the legionella virus cannot survive at this temperature, While you may be shown the main hot-water and central heating systems, keep an eye out on the walkabout for other systems that staff or management may not know about. In one warehouse I found a large gas space-heating system. The warehouse had very large open doors and so masses of heat was being wasted. When I met the owner to discuss the final eco-audit report, the first thing he said was that my figures for gas were wrong as there were no gas heaters in the warehouse. He only acceded when the finance department gave him the figures backing my report.

In a Midlands school that I eco-audited, I found that in addition to the central heating and hot-water system, each of the four children's toilets in the school had their own non-insulated electric hot-water immersion heater. These use between 3,000 and 6,000 watts and so were one of the largest users of electricity in the building, but no one in the school knew that they were there and so they were on 24 hours a day, all year round, even during the school holidays when the building was empty.

Air-conditioning

Air-conditioning is a serious source of energy waste in many office buildings. Various studies have found that a traditionally air-conditioned office building can use up to 100 per cent more energy than a non-air-conditioned building of the same size. With increasingly hot summers in the UK, more managers are coming under pressure from their staff to install air-conditioning systems. If the organization you are eco-auditing is in this position, you need to advise them to look first at measures that could be taken to alleviate the problem without resorting to air-conditioning.

How to reduce heat without air-conditioning

■ Ensure all unnecessary lighting is turned off in summer.

■ Only use low-energy light bulbs and fluorescent tubes.

■ Turn off all unnecessary electronic equipment.

■ Open all available doors and windows to allow the best possible air flow.

■ Use only efficient flat-screen TV monitors and computers.

■ Install Venetian blinds in the windows to block direct sunlight.

■ Install retractable shades over the windows externally to block direct sunlight.

■ If there is space, plant fast-growing deciduous trees to shade the south-facing aspect of the building from direct sunlight.

■ Ensure any shades or curtains on east-facing windows are drawn at night to prevent that section of the building from overheating in the morning sunshine before staff arrive.

■ Ensure that all skylights or windows on upper floors are open during hot days, with doors on the ground floor open, allowing air flow, because heat rises and so needs to be able to escape when it reaches the top of the building.

My experience when eco-auditing a charity in King's Cross, London, demonstrates how it is possible to avoid installing air-conditioning and still lower office temperatures. I was inspecting the office of the finance director, who told me he really needed advice on how to cool the finance office next door. It was a small room with three staff working there. They had three old CTR monitors and PCs, each belting out about 200 watts, and they also had three up-lighters. When I checked, each of the bulbs was rated at 200 watts. Thus the total wattage of the equipment was 1,200 watts or the equivalent of having two electric fires on in the office right through the summer. When you added body heat as well, it was no wonder the office was unbearable. By replacing the lights with energy-saving models and installing flat-screen computers, the energy used could be reduced to about 210 watts, making the room far more pleasant without the use of air-conditioning.

If, despite these suggestions, the company still wants to go ahead and install an air-conditioning system, ask them to consider the new cooled-water-based systems from companies like EcoCooling Ltd. These use up to a tenth of the energy of a refrigerant-based system and have the advantage that they operate with open windows. This is useful, as you will find in many offices with traditional air-conditioning that staff like to have the windows open *and* the air-conditioning on, thus wasting vast amounts of energy. The best way of getting across to people how wasteful this is is to compare it to having the windows wide open at home in the middle of winter with the heating on, as the same loss of energy is involved. Even with the best management systems in the world, if staff are determined to have the windows open and the air-conditioning on, they will. In this case, the cooled-water-based system is the answer. It also has significantly cheaper running and capital costs in comparison with traditional systems. The capital costs can be up to 75 per cent lower. The main drawback is that it cannot operate in very high buildings with sealed windows.

The other issue that will arise in relation to air-conditioning is the temperature it is set at. Most systems are individually controlled, which means that it is very hard to have a fixed policy. But every degree the system is colder than the ambient air means about another 10 per cent on the energy and carbon dioxide costs. So the recommendation here is the opposite to that for central heating: that is, you want the air-conditioning set at as high a temperature as possible – about 25°C should be about right. You will also need to check what systems are in place for ensuring that all air-conditioning units are turned off at night. It is quite common for them to be left running all night, because no one is responsible for ensuring that they are all off at the end of the day.

Lighting

Three main issues tend to arise as you do your workplace walkabout. First, you will probably find that the most energy-efficient bulbs or fluorescent tubes are not being used. Bulbs and lighting tubes now have energy-efficiency ratings on their packaging, just like fridges. Ask whoever is responsible to ensure that they buy only the most efficient, A-rated lighting. In addition, many offices, especially in their reception and public areas, have installed the dreaded halogen down-lighters. These can now be replaced by ultra-efficient LED lamps, which use only about 1.2 watts of electricity, thus saving up to 48 watts per 50-watt halogen lamp if normal electricity is being used. However, most people still find some LED bulbs quite blue and so they will only work in certain workplaces and situations. It is best to experiment with them and the other CFL alternatives, to see what is acceptable. But there is no doubt that the energy saving is enormous.

The second issue concerns light switches. For some reason I have not been able to determine, electricians and lighting designers have a fetish for putting in as few switches as possible. This often means that someone working late by themselves has to have an entire floor of an office block illuminated, just to light one desk. It also means that if new rooms are created by installing partitions, the separate rooms cannot have their lights switched off when they are empty, as that would mean the occupied rooms would also have their lights turned off.

The final issue is that for so much of the time lights are on unnecessarily. I find it extraordinary that large offices now seem to expect the lights to be on all the time regardless of the fact that there are floor to ceiling glass walls and the rooms are flooded with daylight. Gently challenge this practice when doing your walkabout. Some people will argue that they need it because of the glare on their computer screens. This can be addressed by putting anti-glare screens on the monitors, putting anti-glare film on the windows or even more simply by rearranging the desk where the monitor sits. It is also worth looking at the number of light fittings in each room and seeing if that number is needed. It can be fun doing this, finding that people will volunteer to take lamps out because they did not want them in the first place. You will also discover that rooms like storerooms, kitchens and workrooms have their lights on all day but will be only used occasionally. Suggesting more staff training and asking for turn-off signs might work, but it is probably more effective to recommend a small investment in movement sensors, so that the lights go off automatically when no one is using the room.

The same applies to security lighting that is left on all night. Installing movement sensors in addition to light sensors means that if the security system is overlooked by a CCTV system, the security guard will be alerted when the light goes on. Even with up to 98 per cent less energy use, the system is thus more effective in detecting intruders.

IT issues

Energy used for computing is taking up an increasing amount of electricity. Modern flat-screen monitors use a tenth of the energy of old bulky cathode ray tubes. In addition, many companies are moving to replace all PCs with laptops, as these use only about one-third of the energy that a traditional computer used. Ensure the IT department has set all computers at deep energy saving mode. Some companies have also successfully installed WAKE-LAN, which means the computers can be centrally turned on and off. This allows software updates to be installed at night but can also ensure all computers are turned off.

It is also important to check the server room for draughts if it is air-conditioned, and to ensure the temperature setting is not set at lower than the optimum recommended by the manufacturer.

Staff energy structures

One of the problems that often emerges from eco-audits is that in business premises staff always feel empowered to turn on lights and equipment but often feel that it is someone else's job to turn them off. For example, they have no problem turning a light on in a bathroom when entering, but feel they should leave it on when they leave in case someone else wants to use it. The psychology of turning lights off in business premises could merit a essay of its own! Often using technology rather than dealing with the vagaries of human nature will help reduce the stress levels of those in charge of reducing energy consumption. For example, seven-day timers allow you to programme different settings for each day of the week, thus allowing you to set it to be off all day Saturday and Sunday. So if the office was closed at weekends, seven-day timers on office photocopiers would eliminate the need to train staff to turn them off at weekends. Movement sensors, light sensors and timers, involve only a modest outlay, and can be well worth the expense if installed sensibly in appropriate situations.

However, there still need to be management systems in place to ensure that energy is being used wisely in your premises. This is best done through a traditional bottom-up approach. Each relevant section of the building should have a named employee whose job specification includes ensuring that energy is used responsibly. This would cover radiator and air-conditioning controls, turning off unused equipment and unnecessary lighting, and ensuring that everything is shut down at the end of the working day.

One of my favourite stories to demonstrate the need for such an approach comes from an eco-audit I did of a charity in Cardiff. When I inspected the canteen kitchen, I had a look inside the four deep-freezers. Three and a half of them were empty. It emerged that they had switched from hot food to sandwiches about three years previously but no one had thought to turn the empty freezers off, so they had been operating night and day up to the day of the eco-audit!

Companies need a reporting structure that ends, through the relevant director, at the chief executive, who would present to the board an annual eco-audit report at the same time as the annual accounts are being submitted.

Questions to ask

- Is the central heating boiler so old you can justify replacing it in energy-efficiency terms?

- Is the timer for the central heating system set at the minimum hours compatible with staff needs?

- Is the timer for the water-heating system set at the minimum hours compatible with staff needs?

- Is the temperature of the hot-water system set at 60°C and not any higher?

- Are the office temperature controls set at 19°C in winter?

- Is the air-conditioning system set no lower than 23°C in summer?

- Does all lighting in the premises use low-energy bulbs or tubes?

- Are the windows and doors kept shut in summer if air-conditioning is left on?

- Are all doors and windows properly draught-proofed and double-glazed?

- Are there named employees with responsibility for energy efficiency in each relevant section of the premises?

- Is all relevant electrical equipment turned off at night and weekends?

Chapter 8

Generating your own eco-energy

Renewable energy solutions

One of the most common reasons domestic household clients give me for hiring an eco-auditor is that they want advice on what renewable energy solutions might be practical for their home. Having read about windmills and solar panels in the media or seen manufacturers' claims on the internet, they feel they need some independent advice on the next step to take. Charities, schools and businesses also often want information on renewable energy technologies that might be suitable for them. So it is important for you to be fully informed when carrying out your audit.

When someone specifically requests a renewable energy consultation for their home, I usually explain that I prefer to carry out a wider eco-audit, which will cover every aspect of their lifestyle and in the process include advice on what forms of renewable energy might be suitable for them. Most people accept this, but you might find that people who have just bought a new home, are planning a major refurbishment or extension at their existing home or indeed are building a new home from scratch want to concentrate solely on renewables. With all of them I repeat my fundamental mantra about the relative costs and benefits of reducing carbon dioxide emissions.

• Reducing energy use through lifestyle choices such as turning down the central heating thermostat, closing the doors of unused rooms and turning radiators off will cost nothing and actually save money – as much as 40 per cent of energy emissions.

• Simple basic energy-efficiency measures such as installing energy-saving bulbs, loft insulation and double glazing will again save up to 40 per cent for a low to medium investment.

• A reduction of between 15 and 20 per cent of carbon dioxide emissions can sometimes be achieved through renewable energy technologies, but this approach is up to 15 times more expensive than simple efficiency measures.

Of course, these are broad estimates and individual situations will vary, but the general message is valid. It is really important to get across to people that the elimination of waste is the easiest and most cost-effective means of slashing our carbon dioxide emissions. For new buildings the equivalent philosophy is to reduce the need for energy in the first place by prioritizing low-energy options.

Having said all this, I am a great supporter of anyone rich enough and enthusiastic about doing their bit to save the planet, who wants to go the final furlong and install renewable energies in their home. They will be making a valuable contribution not only to reducing their own carbon footprint but also to making the technologies cheaper for everyone else. As with any product, the more people buy it, the cheaper it becomes. You just need to be aware of the relative cost benefits of the different approaches.

What is renewable energy?

It might seem odd, but to answer this question we first need to define non-renewable energy. Non-renewable energy systems are those that consume resources that cannot be replaced. The main examples are systems powered by nuclear and fossil fuels. There is only so much uranium, oil, natural gas, peat and coal on the planet; once these run out, future generations will have no way of renewing their supplies – hence the term non-renewable.

From this it follows that systems using forms of energy that are constantly being renewed, such as wind, solar and biomass (plant materials), are renewable energy systems. The sun will continue to shine no matter how much we use solar power to create electricity and hot water; the wind will continue to blow no matter how many wind turbines we build; and we can keep planting bio-fuel crops and trees after we have used them to power our cars and fuel our central heating boilers.

Before being able to reach a decision about which renewable energy solutions to pursue, you need to know what each of them can provide.

Solar thermal panels

By far the most common renewable energy technology in the UK – over 75,000 of the 80,000 domestic renewable energy systems installed by 2006 – solar thermal panels produce hot water. There are two main types: flat-plate collectors and evacuated-tube collectors. Both require a site that is generally south-facing, not overshadowed and ideally at an angle of about 30°. If you have a flat roof, it is possible to install a frame to enable the panel to be angled correctly, but this can raise issues in relation to planning permission.

Flat-plate collectors

These consist of a highly absorptive metal plate with copper tubing bonded at the rear. It is often made up of a metal radiator, about 1 metre by 0.33 metres, which is painted black and set in a glass casing. This is placed where it will get maximum exposure to sunshine (unsurprisingly, usually on a roof!), at an angle of about 30° and ideally facing directly south. Placing it at this angle ensures the longest exposure to the rays of the sun. Water is then trickled through the radiator, which heats it up for use within the home, for showers, washing up and so on. An electric pump usually pumps the water up to the radiator, from which it returns back down via piping to a hot-water storage tank, which should be very well insulated. The better the insulation, the longer the water will stay hot. Depending on use, it can continue to provide hot water for a couple of days even if the weather becomes cloudy.

Evacuated-tube collectors

These look similar to flat-plate collectors in that they are made up of a panel about 1 metre by 0.33 metres, although larger houses sometimes have two panels joined together. This time, however, each panel contains a series of strong glass tubes that have been evacuated and have an efficient heat conductor attached, designed to trap more radiation heat. The vacuum created in the tubing makes them considerably more efficient than the flat-plate collectors but they are also more expensive.

The piping at the back of the tubes is usually connected to a heat-exchanger within the hot-water storage tank, where the water is heated. In other words, the liquid that is pumped up to the panel on the roof is heated by the sun and, as it passes back down through the tubing in the water tank, it heats the hot water there, which can then be used in the building. The electric pump used to pump either hot water or anti-freeze through the pipes is normally powered by mains electricity, which means that the system is not completely carbon neutral; it also means that if the system is operating and the hot water is not used, some carbon dioxide will have been released for no purpose. One way round this is to power the electric pump by a solar photovoltaic panel (see page 194). This will store the electricity generated from the sun in a battery that the electric pump can draw on for energy. Early systems worked on the basis that when the sun was out, the pump went into action, but it was soon realized that if the tank was hotter than the roof on cold winter days, when the sun came out the heat-exchange system would operate in reverse and heat would be taken from the hot-water tank to the roof! As this meant possibly losing the heat being provided by the supplementary back-up system in winter, a refinement had to be devised.

Most modern systems now have a thermostatic control incorporated, which means that the electric pump will not kick in unless the temperature of the water at the bottom of the hot-water tank is a good 5°C colder than the temperature of the liquid in the panel on the roof. With such systems, even in temperate northern Europe, a significant contribution to heating water can be made in the middle of winter on the odd sunny day. Last Christmas Day, my solar thermal panels had preheated the water to 20°C, which meant I only had to use the back-up system to increase it another 19 degrees to a showering temperature of about 39°C, and as early as Easter this year, with a burst of spring sunshine, I had to mix in cold water to bring the temperature down from 56°C to be able to shower.

Many people do not realize how much energy is used in heating hot water. The average kettle uses about 2,500 watts of electricity to power it continuously for as long as it is boiling, which means it uses the same amount of energy as about 250 energy-saving bulbs. An electric immersion water heater will use two metal electric heating elements of the sort in a kettle, each of which will use about 3,000 watts. So leaving the hot-water tank on unnecessarily can be the equivalent of having 600 energy-saving bulbs on continuously. This illustration shows how important it is to use hot water and immersion heaters wisely, and should really bring home what a miracle it is that we can actually create the same level of hot water by simply harnessing the heat of the sun. I had not realized the scale of carbon emissions involved in heating hot water until I had my solar electric system installed and saw the LED meter reading for how much energy the house was using when I turned on the electric kettle go almost off the scale.

While integrating a solar photovoltaic system into the household's electricity supply is really simple, choosing and installing a solar hot-water system can be quite complex. You will have to make a number of technical decisions: how many solar-heating panels, how big a tank, where to locate the hot-water tank, what type of back-up system, how to power the pump and so on. Make sure you talk to the company who is supplying a quote and get answers that relate specifically to your requirements.

In normal years in the UK between early May and early October a solar hot-water system should be able to provide you with nearly all your regular needs. The industry claims that systems can provide up to 70 per cent of hot-water requirements over the entire year and certainly this has been my experience with the system I had installed in my own home. It is important to note that you will need a warm-feed washing machine or dishwasher if you want to use the hot water from the roof to supply these machines. Unfortunately, most machines are cold-feed only, which means they take in cold water and heat it, using electricity.

Some people wonder about using solar hot water with the central heating system. The solar hot-water system will not make a huge contribution to raising the temperature for a radiator-based central heating system, as it is obviously most effective in the late spring, summer and early autumn, when you will not usually need any space heating. However, if you have an underfloor piped heating system it can make a useful contri-bution, as this system uses water at about 40°C, whereas radiator systems need water at 60°C. You will nearly always need a back-up hot-water system for winter and cloudy days. This can be provided by a gas, oil or electric hot-water system or preferably biomass. Worcester Bosch was one of the first major engineering companies to introduce an integrated solar hot-water and central heating system. If you are buying a new central heating system but want to install a solar hot-water system later, you need to ensure that the central heating boiler can be retro-fitted as you will need both systems to be integrated to get the maximum benefit. At the very least this usually means that it can take a hot as well as a cold feed, otherwise it will not be able to accept the preheated hot water from the solar system.

As in most industries, the solar hot-water installation industry has the occasional shark. I have been phoned by people who have had useless systems installed. The problem was usually that the installer had put the panels so far away from the shower or hot-water taps that the water was cold by the time it got there.

Always ask for references, get a personal recommendation or check that your installer is approved by the Energy Saving Trust and/or is a member of the Solar Trade Association. In 2007 in the UK you could expect to spend between £2,500 and £5,000 to install a solar hot-water system.

Solar photovoltaic (PV) panels

While solar thermal panels provide hot water, solar photovoltaic panels (also called solar electric panels) produce electricity in DC (direct current) format, which is the type of electricity produced by batteries. Inverters are then used to convert this to AC (alternating current) electricity, which is the type of electricity used in homes and businesses. This is necessary as DC systems require completely different wiring and electrical goods, and it is totally impractical, prohibitively expensive, not to mention environmentally irresponsible to ask anyone to rewire their homes and throw out all their existing electrical goods merely to take advantage of some solar electricity produced on the roof.

Using the standard solar PV technology we have today, enough electricity to power all the electrical usage in the United States could be provided with photovoltaic power plants covering about 30,000 square kilometres of roofing or land. In 1839 the French scientist Alexandre-Edmond Becquerel discovered that sunlight could produce an electrical current in a solid material. This is known as the photovoltaic effect and is how a PV solar cell converts sunlight into electricity. When light shines on a PV cell, it can be reflected, absorbed or pass through it. The absorbed light generates electricity. In the early 1950s PV cells were developed as a spin-off from transistor technology. A single PV cell is a thin semi-conductor wafer of two layers generally made of highly purified silicon (PV cells can be made of many different semi-conductors but crystalline silicon is the most widely used). Silicon is made from sand, which is the second most common material on the planet after water. The layers are sandwiched between boron on one side and phosphorus on the other side, producing a surplus of electrons on one side and a deficit of electrons on the other side.

When the wafer is exposed to sunlight, the photons in the sunlight knock off some of the excess electrons. This makes a voltage difference between the two sides as the excess electrons try to move to the deficit side, thus creating an electric current. Metallic contacts are made on both sides of the semi-conductor cell. With an external circuit attached to the contacts, the electrons can get back to where they came from and a current flows through the circuit. The bigger the cell, the more efficient the cells or the more intense the sunlight that they are exposed to, the more electrons generated and so the more electricity produced. Simple really!

A solar electric panel consists of many PV cells wired in parallel to increase current and in series to produce a higher voltage. The cells are encapsulated with tempered glass (or some other transparent material) on the front surface and usually placed in an aluminium frame. On the back of the module there is a junction box or wire leads, providing electrical connections, from which the electricity is conducted to the inverter and from there to be used in the house. At present the amount of the sun's light that is converted to useable electricity varies from about 12 to 18 per cent, but research is being carried out to improve efficiencies all the time.

Panels made by different manufacturers can be intermixed without any problem, as long as all the modules have rated voltage output within a 1-volt difference. Unlike solar thermal panels, which will produce plenty of hot water with just one or two panels, each solar PV panel is rated at about 110–200 watts. This means between seven and 15 panels would normally be installed to produce the 750–1,600 watts expected of such a system. This means that a solar PV arrangement will take up a great deal more roof space than a solar hot-water system. It is worth noting when considering how many panels you should install that solar electric panels usually only produce a maximum of about 70–80 per cent of their stated wattage rating.

Like solar thermal panels, they should be located where there is no threat of overshadowing by adjacent buildings, trees and chimneys or by dormer windows on the building itself. Trees can always be pruned and chimneys could even be removed, but it makes no sense to install solar electric panels if they are going to be seriously overshadowed for a part of the day. In borderline cases, it is best to call in a solar installation expert who you can trust to be honest. Do not despair if you have a flat roof, as frames exist that will position the panels at the optimum angle, provided of course that the flat roof itself is not seriously overshadowed.

Once the electricity has been generated, you then have to consider what inverters to use. In the early days, there would have been only one large or at most two inverters for each household roof installation. Now, however, there are small inverters that can be attached to each panel, ensuring that if a shadow falls on one solar panel all the others do not go down, as can happen if you have only one inverter. This can help to increase the efficiency of the system by up to 10 per cent.

Originally solar electric technology was a costly source of power for satellites but it has come down steadily in price, making it affordable as a source of some power to homes and businesses. Indeed, as long ago as 2001 KPMG carried out a cost-effectiveness study and found that, even at 2001 oil prices (which had not yet rocketed as a result of the war in Iraq), PV was techno-logically competitive with oil. The reason why it was not yet competitive financially was market failure. In other words, there was not yet a big enough production facility to manufacture the chips and panels in sufficiently large numbers for the price to come down, nor was there yet enough demand to justify the commercial risk in building such a plant: a classic market blockage. It is a sign of how little importance governments attach to this issue that such a plant has yet to be built. In 2001 it would have cost about £350 million or half the cost of the Millennium Dome, the huge white elephant that the UK government unfortunately built to mark the millennium in London.

Governments could do two things. First, they could enter into a joint venture to build such a plant; and second, where practical they could require all new buildings to include such panels. At a stroke, this would help slash the price of the technology and provide a stable, lucrative new market. Having fulfilled government's role of sorting out a market blockage for a product that society desperately needs, it could then bow out and allow the market its rightful role, delivering a service at a competitive rate, having established a regulatory framework. There would probably need to be continued support for the retro-fitting of existing homes; this could be done through a grants system or by requiring the electricity companies to pay a premium for electricity exported from such systems into the national grid.

While waiting for governments to act or for the market to unblock, there is nothing to stop better-off consumers and environmental activists investing in the technology even if it is expensive. The average domestic installation in the UK costs about £13,000 for a 2-kW-rated system, excluding any grants that may be available from local or national government. This means that, at an ideal temperature and sunshine exposure, such a system would produce 2 kW of electricity per hour. Over a year this would produce in total about 1,500 kWh in southern England or about a third of the average English family's electricity consumption. At 2007 electricity prices that would be worth about £150 if it was all used on site. Remember, that this is a third of total *electricity* consumption and not total energy consumption. Even if you get a grant the payback period at current capital costs would be at least 85 years. People install PV at current prices because they want to save the planet and not because they want to save their pockets. However, systems are coming down in price in real terms year by year, as more and more people buy them. They are also becoming more and more efficient. Modern panels now produce 65 per cent more electricity per square metre than they did ten years ago, when I installed my system. These improvements would never have happened if people did not go ahead and buy the technology in its early expensive stages.

If you decide there is potential for solar technology in the premises you are eco-auditing, you need to contact a contractor to assess the property in detail. Some contractors will do this site visit and quotation for free. You should only recommend trusted installers and those who have been accredited properly.

Wind turbines

There has been a lot of excitement in the UK recently about the possibility of installing small wind turbines on urban houses. I confess to having contributed a little to this excitement, as my house was the first in London to get planning permission for a building-attached micro-turbine. The wind turbine was installed in November 2005 amid a huge amount of media interest, but unfortunately I have to be honest and say it has been quite a disappointment to date. In the last five months only about 10 kWh or £1 worth of electricity has been produced, which is a pretty poor payback, to say the least, for an investment of just under £3,000. The model installed (an Eclectic Energy D400 Stealthgen) has been turning nicely in the wind, unlike some other small domestic turbines I have read about, and it has been really quiet, with no complaints from the neighbours. There have been some internal vibration issues, which have led to its being turned off during the night, further reducing output.

Although research is being carried out to improve performance, my advice is to avoid investing in domestic building-attached wind turbines until such time as you have seen independent evidence guaranteeing a decent output for wind speeds in your area.

One major problem is that micro-wind turbines need an inverter that can cope with the rapid swings in power output inherent with urban wind. Different companies are working to resolve this. Some commentators say the technology will never deliver but I think the jury is still out. It is early days and the companies developing the technology are tiny. Meanwhile, I view my own turbine as a beautiful spinning sculpture. It represents my passion to tackle the climate crisis, and is a reminder that through my other technologies my home is now almost zero-carbon. However, there are currently far more effective ways of spending £3,000 to reduce your carbon footprint.

This does not mean ruling out wind energy in every domestic situation, but you will need to have a reasonable plot of land beside your home to allow the erection of a large pole to get the wind turbine as high as possible and a very good supply of uninterrupted wind. The higher the better, as the energy produced multiplies exponentially the higher the turbine. In the UK, the Department of Trade and Industry has an excellent website on which people can find out via their postcode the average wind speeds in their area. This, however, will only provide a rough guide and if you are seriously thinking of investing in a medium-sized wind turbine, which will cost from about £20,000 upwards, you really need to get site-specific data on the amount of wind available over the year. Remember that in most sites the wind will only be blowing for about a third of the year, but obviously the best sites will be on the windy sides of hills and mountains or those sites exposed to onshore winds.

Small battery-charging wind turbines have long been used for powering lights and other equipment on board yachts. Eclectic

Energy is one of the UK's leading suppliers of such DC wind turbines. Proven Energy are among the leading manufacturers of small to medium-sized wind turbines in Britain, with machines rated at 600 watts, 2.5 kW and 6 kW. The tower heights vary from 5 to 25 metres. They recommend siting the turbines at least 20 metres from the house, so they are definitely not suitable for the average urban home. However, they work really well in windy coastal sites and on exposed hillsides. You need a minimum wind speed of about 6 metres per second at an exposed height of 10 metres to make them feasible. Most urban areas in the UK will not have such wind speeds, although exposed sites along the water-front in cities like Liverpool and Blackpool are exceptions. The electricity generated can be stored in batteries, but by using an inverter it can be exported to the national grid or used to create heat during windy periods.

Wood-burners

Wood is the renewable energy that many people forget about. With the media full of images of sexy solar panels and wind turbines, the humble wood-burner is nearly always overlooked, but it is an excellent source of renewable heat. In addition, burning wood is basically carbon neutral in that you are burning wood from trees that have stored carbon dioxide from the atmosphere and which would have been returned to the atmosphere anyway when the trees died and decomposed. So burning non-virgin forest wood is not adding to the total amount of carbon dioxide in the atmosphere, unlike the burning of fossil fuels, which releases the carbon dioxide deposited over literally millions of years in coal, peat, oil and gas. In addition, the burning of wood helps to create local markets for timber in countries like the UK, where the wood that is burned is generally not used for other purposes, such as furniture or paper manufacture. Obviously, this does not apply to the burning down of virgin temperate forests and rainforests, which disasterously reduces the overall amount of carbon dioxide stored in forests and is one of the biggest contributors to total global greenhouse gas emissions.

If your home is in the country, it is quite likely that you will already have a source of wood nearby, if not on your own property. If the trees are located on your own property, the wood will be a free source of fuel. Ideally you should use dead trees and fallen branches first, but then you can coppice the existing trees without having to fell them. This is what was done in medieval times. Coppicing means simply harvesting major branches from a tree, while allowing it to continue to grow. It is the most sustainable way of harvesting firewood.

There are two main approaches to using wood for space and water heating in domestic homes: the wood-burning stove and wood-powered central heating.

Wood-burning stove or space heater

The traditional metal wood-burner is your simplest – and cheapest – option. Modern versions with a glass door, through which you can watch the wood burn, provide a really cosy heart to a room. If you have a wood-burner with a flat top, then this can be used as a stove to boil water and even to cook, as temperatures will reach as high as 500°C. If you are careful, you can make delicious toast, but you have to keep an eagle eye out if you want to avoid blackened cinder! There are also specifically designed wood-burning cookers, which can also have a back-burner for hot water or to heat radiators in other rooms.

The fire, which is very easily lit, does require feeding with chopped wood every half-hour or so, but if it goes out it can be relit in a couple of minutes. You certainly do not have to wait hours for the embers to cool down, as is the case with coal fires, before resetting the fire. The ash has to be emptied about every three to four weeks and can be used as a mulch or thrown on the compost heap. As the ash in the grate accumulates, efficiency decreases because it increasingly blocks the access to the air that is essential for combustion.

Some wood-burners can also have a back-boiler installed and this can be used to heat water to supply space-heating radiators in other parts of the building or for use around the house. Obviously, back-boilers are difficult to retro-fit, so it is best to include them when a house is being built or refurbished. Opinions vary on their merits: some people swear by them, while others say that they significantly reduce the efficiency of the burner as a room heater. Obviously, if the piping is not already in place, the installation of such an additional feature to the wood-burner will be costly and also increase the amount of upheaval involved for the household.

For those who live in built-up parts of the UK, certain makes of high-temperature stoves are legal in smoke-free zones. These are up to twice the price of the standard stove used in rural, non-smoke-controlled areas. In the UK, room wood-burning stoves currently cost between £400 and about £1,500, but the installation can cost far more, depending on the condition and height of the chimney. If the chimney is quite old, it is worth installing a metal chimney liner, which will significantly reduce the fire risk associated with burning wood, but they do not come cheap.

What is definitely worth having is an Ecofan. This amazing little gizmo uses the heat of the stove to turn its fans and then blows warm air all round the house, thus resolving one of the chief drawbacks to wood-burners: that although they are very good at heating the space immediately beside and above them, the heat does not travel far. The Ecofan works on the thermocouple principle that if two different metals are at different temperatures, a small electric current will be created, which then powers the fan, simply using the heat of the stove, and so is carbon neutral.

For safety reasons wood-burners, just like gas boilers, have to be installed by qualified technicians. In the UK the quality standard scheme is run by an organization called HETAS (Heating Equipment Testing and Approval Scheme). Their website will provide a list of accredited wood-burner installers in your area.

Wood-powered central heating systems

There are now fully automated wood-powered central heating boilers on the market that use pellets, chips, logs or a mixture of these. A hopper feeds fuel into the system automatically, while the controls are very similar to those of an oil or gas-fired boiler. The main restraints are local availability of fuel, the space required to store the fuel and also the space required for the boiler, which is significantly bigger than a gas boiler.

Like most central heating boilers, they can be used to heat hot water, but as you will not want to be using the heating system in the summer, a back-up hot-water system should be considered. If money is no object, a solar hot-water system would complement things nicely, with winter hot water coming from the wood-powered central heating system and summer hot water from the solar thermal panels.

As not many wood-burning central heating systems have been installed yet in the UK, the process is still very expensive, with prices currently ranging from about £10,000 to £18,000. The great advantage is that they are carbon neutral, so in rural situations, where wood is freely available, they are ideal if finances allow. Somerset County Council, which has installed a number of these on its premises, says that it has found that running costs are less than that for fossil fuels.

Heat pumps

Heat pumps use heat-exchangers to step up the background temperature of the ground or the air to heat water or provide space heating. There are two different types in use: ground-source and air heat pumps.

Ground-source heat pumps

The temperature of the soil in the UK, once you go down about a metre, is a constant 10°C, no matter what the temperature of the air above. One kind of ground-source heat pump uses a system of piping laid out at that depth in the garden, through which water is pumped to collect this constant latent heat. The water is then brought back through the piping to the heat-exchanger in the room where the machinery is placed, where it is stepped up to the temperature required. The technology is basically the same as a fridge but in reverse. This system is often used in conjunction with underfloor central heating, which requires lower water temperatures of about 40°C, rather than the more usual 60°C required by traditional radiator-based systems as mentioned before.

Many people have heard about these heat pumps and are excited about the possibility of installing such a system, as they think it sounds like free space and water heating. However, it is important to remember that even once the very large capital costs have been taken into account, ground-source heat pumps do not run for free, unlike solar electric panels. The problem is that significant amounts of water have to be pumped through the system to capture the heat in the soil. It is estimated that for each unit of electrical energy you put in, you get about three to four units of heat energy out. On the face of it, this still sounds like a good deal, but unfortunately the pump will usually use mains electricity, which is normally produced from a fossil-fuel source.

Power stations lose between 40 and 65 per cent of the energy stored in their coal or gas before it is converted into electricity. In addition, significant amounts disappear in what are called transmission losses, due to the resistances in the electric wiring, and more energy is lost in the pump, as the electrical energy is converted back into the mechanical energy. Thus, by most calculations, you are actually inputting up to three units of energy to get about four out. This might still sound good, but then you have to realize that if you are only making a net energy profit of one unit for the three you have put in, then this unit of heat energy must be used almost 100 per cent effectively. And how many homes use all their hot water or their space heating effectively? In my experience it is almost impossible to do so, which means that you could end up in a situation where you are putting in the same amount of – if not more – energy than you are getting out and actually using.

So unfortunately, as with domestic wind turbines in most circumstances, my reluctant advice at this stage for most homes is that the significant capital costs of installing a ground-source heat system (from about £6,000–£18,000) and the nuisance of laying a large array of piping underneath the garden do not make much sense. What is more, many homes will not have large enough gardens to accommodate the piping required. And where homes have a supply of town gas, it is true to say that currently ground-source heat pumps generally do not make sense, not only in financial terms but also, even more importantly, in terms of carbon dioxide emissions – in other words, people could end up emitting more carbon dioxide by using an electrically powered heat pump than if they had the latest ultra-efficient condensing gas boiler. This does not rule heat pumps out in all circumstances. For example, a home might have a very effective micro-hydroelectric system or a large, effective stand-alone wind turbine with plenty of spare renewable energy capacity after the electrical appliances have been powered, in which case they could run the electrical pump without having to import electricity.

A second type of ground-source heat pump involves drilling down directly into the ground for about 65 metres and feeding the pipes down into this hole and up again, rather than laying them flat a metre below the surface of the garden. This reduces the area needed for installing the system, but the other caveats apply. In addition you would need to get a drilling rig into the garden, with all the cost and access implications involved.

Air heat pump

Much simpler and smaller than a ground-source heat pump, this uses the background heat of the air, which is increased, through heat-exchangers, to the temperature required. Some of the caveats that apply to ground-source heat pumps apply here.

Micro-hydro generators

A more unusual source of home eco-energy is micro-hydro, which is the generation of electricity from small (up to 100 kWh) water-powered electric turbines. Obviously, this will not be on the agenda for the vast majority of urban-based households, but if you are carrying out a rural eco-audit, it is important to check whether the property or anything adjacent to it has any streams or small rivers that could be harnessed.

My old boss had a friend with a farm in the Welsh hills that produced so much energy in winter from a small water generator that there was often enough left over after covering all the household requirements to power storage heaters in the barns to make the cows cosy! Of course, that was in the days before you could sell surplus electricity to the national grid – and you can now make a tidy profit on it too.

Water has been a source of industrial power for centuries. In the UK there were over 20,000 water-wheels operating at one stage. With the development of huge fossil-fuelled power stations these became obsolete and most have long since closed and fallen into disuse. But with the development of efficient small micro-hydro turbines and an urgent need to move away from burning fossil fuels, the generation of power from the water in rivers and streams is again becoming an exciting reality in many projects across the UK. Basically, a micro-hydro turbine converts the energy stored by gravity in the water into mechanical energy by using it to turn a turbine, which in turn is used to generate electricity. As with other forms of home generation, this energy can be used in the home or, if too much is produced, it can be exported to the national grid, which will help pay the initial capital costs. Like most emerging technologies, it is certainly not cheap yet, with small-scale projects currently costing between £10,000 and £30,000.

There are three key questions that need answering for micro-hydro projects:

• What is the head of the water – i.e. what is the fall in metres between the highest point of the water and the exit from the turbine?

• What is the flow of water in cubic metres per second?

• For what percentage of the year is the average flow maintained?

The answers determine the potential output of the system and the economic viability of installing it. Two specific types of property are currently attracting attention in this area: old water-mill sites, which already have a lot of the infrastructure in place (e.g. the mill pond, mill race, etc.) and hill properties with fast-flowing streams that have a good head of water. Some grants from the government are available for the installation of such systems, but an abstraction licence will normally be required.

Grid connection

With the renewable electrical energy systems outlined above, you need to know about grid-connection issues. A grid-connected renewable electrical system is one where the electricity has been converted from DC energy, produced by the equipment, to AC electricity, which can be exported from the premises to the national grid. This is something well worth considering, because at times your system will produce more energy than you can use. It is much easier to export it to the national grid and be paid for it than installing a whole series of inefficient batteries, with the accompanying capital costs.

Many of the electricity supply companies will now buy such electricity. There is a whole range of ways they do this and it can be a minefield trying to figure out which is the best deal for you. Systems vary, from having a meter installed that measures how much is being exported to systems that estimate the annual output and pay for it on that basis. One of the best renewable electricity supply companies, Good Energy, has a special programme to buy electricity from small domestic producers.

Usually once you have decided which company you wish to sell your surplus electricity to, your installer will liaise with the national grid authorities and deal with the relevant bureaucracy. Having a grid-connected system means that you cannot remain functioning if the national grid goes down, as there would be a danger of electrocuting a grid engineer who did not know the property was still live. Thus the regulations require grid-connected systems to close down automatically if the national grid is down in the property's neighbourhood.

Unfortunately, the price paid to domestic exporters in the UK is significantly less than the price customers pay for their own imported electricity, unlike in Germany, where a hefty premium is paid. This means that payback periods in the UK, which exceed 80 years, can be as low as 20 in Germany. It also means that in the UK you would have to export almost twice as much electricity as you buy before even breaking even on electricity usage, never mind starting to address capital payback periods.

Planning issues

Some renewable energy systems – for example, all wind turbines – require planning permission. The situation with regard to solar panels is more complex, as it depends on your local authority. You are always entitled to write and ask for an exemption from planning permission if the property is not in a conservation area, is not a listed building and if the solar installation does not alter the line of the roof. Some progressive councils exempt as a matter of policy all such solar panels from requiring planning permission and others decide on a case-by-case basis. You need their letter confirming exemption before you go ahead. However, there are other councils that require planning for all such installations and often – inexplicably and sadly – they have policies opposing installation in many circumstances.

Plenty of people are pressing the government to change this situation, so that planning permission is not required. You will need to check with your local council to see what the situation is in your area. The regulations are, however, currently being reviewed by the government with a view to relaxing them. Always check with your local council as to what the current situation is.

If you want to get planning permission for a wind turbine or solar panel on your property, a good tip is to inform all the affected neighbours yourself, so they hear about the project and the details from you first and not in an anonymous threatening letter from the council. This really helps build trust and support, as I found to my delight when I got planning permission for the first building-mounted wind turbine in London. Solar hot-water roof tiles, which have just come on the market, and solar electric roof tiles will avoid many of the planning hurdles facing solar panels.

Conclusion

While many of these technologies are new and often expensive, there is nothing to beat the satisfaction of knowing that you are producing your own home or company's heat or electricity. As a professional eco-auditor, I find supporting clients who are enthusiastic, while providing them with the cold, hard facts about practicality and the economics of their situation, one of the most exciting aspects of my job.

Sample costs for installed domestic renewable energy systems

System	Cost
Wood-burning stove or space heater	£500–3,000
DC yacht wind turbine	£2,000
Domestic micro-wind turbine	£3,000
Solar hot-water system	£4,000
5-kW micro-hydro turbine	£10,000
2.5-kW pole turbine	£11,000
2-kW solar electric PV system	£12,000
Wood-burning central heating boiler	£13,000
Ground-source heat pump system	£6,000–18,000
6-kW pole turbine	£19,000

Modest grants of between 10 and 20 per cent are currently available for most of these, with the exception of wood-burners and wind turbines rated under 0.5 kW. However, the UK government has announced that these will be abolished in due course.

Ironically, the most effective of the technologies listed in the box above is the cheapest. Pound for pound, a wood-burning stove is by far the cheapest technology for reducing your household carbon emissions. The government grants are currently available not only to domestic homes but also to businesses, charities and other organizations.

Chapter 9

Transport

Transport and the environment

Transport will contribute up to about a third of total energy carbon dioxide emissions for the average household eco-audit. Obviously, the percentage will vary for organizations depending on the nature of their business; for some it will make up the bulk of their emissions. Thus it is crucial that you are up to speed on the environmental issues surrounding transport.

The fossil fuels used to power our cars, trucks, ships and planes make up about 25 per cent of total global carbon dioxide emissions. Vehicle emissions are measured in grams of CO_2 per kilometre, the average in the EU being 162 grams for every kilometre driven. Only 481 of the 2.5 million cars sold in the UK in 2005 emitted less than 100 grams per kilometre, qualifying them for the lowest (zero) tax band. In both home and work transport eco-audits, you need to identify the vehicle with the lowest practical emissions. Most cars on sale now fall somewhere between about 100 and 360 grams per kilometre. Choosing a top of the range 4x4, with emissions over four times higher than the most economical cars available, is just not viable in light of the crisis we are facing. But not all 4x4s are automatically very bad; some emit from 190 grams per kilometre. Thus changing from one brand of 4x4 to another could cut CO_2 emissions by over 50 per cent. The key thing prior to choosing a car is to check the range of emissions in the class of car you are looking for. The lower the emissions band, the lower the annual vehicle excise duty. While manufacturers have slowly been making cars more efficient, we have at the same time been driving them in greater numbers and we are buying bigger and bigger cars, so the gains have been more than wiped out. In 1980 there were 15 million cars on UK roads, but by 2005 this had increased to a whopping 33 million!

Just as Britain has followed America into the destructive car economy, so India and China now seem to be catching up fast, with hundreds of millions of people set to adopt a car-based lifestyle in the developing world. There is no doubt that the invention of the internal combustion engine and the jet engine has brought about an extraordinary revolution in how far and how cheaply we can move about the planet. But this amazing freedom has been bought at a huge price, and not only in terms of the massive contribution to the accumulation of greenhouse gases. Millions have been killed and injured since Ford first launched its mass-market cars, while the resulting pollution has been directly linked to millions more deaths from respiratory diseases. There are over 280,000 injuries and 3,000 deaths on UK roads alone every year.

Flying

While it currently makes up only about 4 per cent of global greenhouse emissions, flying is one of the fastest-growing contributors to the climate crisis. The relatively small figure is because just a tenth of the world's population has access to the wealth that allows people to fly, but for those who do fly, the emissions can be enormous. For example, if a family of four make a return flight from London to Tokyo, they would be responsible for the emission of 8 tonnes of carbon dioxide, which is 33 per cent more than the average home emits in an entire year! In addition, the small, rich elite who can afford to fly are now flying more and more often every year, following the introduction of cheap, no-frills airlines. This practice, which has led to an explosion of air travel within Europe, is now being introduced for transatlantic flights, which will have similar results unless airlines are made to pay the true economic and environmental cost of their climate-crisis-causing gases.

Across the globe, some 16,700 planes fly every day. This is predicted to increase to over 27,000 by 2025. Meanwhile, Britons are predicted to take over 100 million foreign trips a year by 2020 and UK aviation to emit 43 million tonnes of carbon by 2050, which equates to two-thirds of the government's targeted reductions for the whole economy. So even though, like cars, planes are gradually getting more efficient, this increase in efficiency is being completely overshadowed by the massive upsurge in numbers of people flying. So where we should urgently be cutting total aviation emissions, we are actually increasing them exponentially. The situation is so bad that scientists are predicting that by 2050 aviation will be the single biggest source worldwide of greenhouse gases, overtaking electricity production and cars and trucks. Indeed, the Tyndall Centre for Climate Change Research estimates that UK aviation emissions by 2050 will be such that all other sectors have to reduce their emissions to zero if the country is to take seriously its need to reduce total emissions to a level that is safe for the planet.

Tips to cut plane emissions

1 Take the train. Emissions from train journeys are about a tenth those of planes. Over 7.5 million people already travel by Eurostar each year from the UK to continental Europe, thus saving huge amounts of carbon dioxide. Rail is becoming increasingly popular as more people understand the environmental benefits and take advantage of the less stressful travelling conditions. Rail passenger numbers in the UK have nearly doubled since 1985, with over a billion journeys being taken by train in 2006.

2 Consider a cycling holiday instead of flying.

3 Go economy. Flying first-class uses up to 50 per cent more fuel because a first-class seat takes up the space of one and a half economy seats.

4 Take less luggage. The greater the weight a plane carries, the more fuel it requires. If everyone takes their 20 kilograms, that is the equivalent of a third of the planeload of passengers. It is possible to get down to one piece of hand luggage, even for a two-week sun holiday.

5 Travel with budget airlines. They usually have a higher proportion of new, more fuel-efficient planes and their flights are usually fuller, thus cutting emissions per kilometre per passenger.

6 Go direct. Do this if possible, rather than using a large airport hub for shorter flights: taking off and landing use more fuel.

7 If you have to fly long haul, the opposite holds true. Huge amounts of extra fuel are required to carry the fuel necessary for long flights, so it is better to break your flight.

8 Ensure that you pay for carbon offsetting. In the absence of taxation on aviation fuel, this means that at least the polluter pays.

9 Use trains rather than planes for onward journeys once you arrive.

10 Avoid private jets at all costs. They use up to 120 times the CO_2 of a long-haul flight!

Cruises

Having decided to avoid planes where possible, you might decide that an ocean-going cruise ship is the perfect alternative for a conscience-free holiday. Unfortunately, much as I would like it to be, this is not the case. An ocean-going liner uses up to ten times more carbon dioxide than a long-haul flight, according to the World Land Trust. In addition, the organization Responsible Travel has estimated that on a typical one-week voyage a cruise ship generates more than 50 tonnes of rubbish, a million litres of waste water, 955,000 litres of sewage waste and 160,000 litres of oil-contaminated water. On average, passengers on a cruise ship each account for 3.5 kilograms of rubbish every day – compared with less than 1 kilogram by local people on shore.

Cruise liners also cause significant damage to coral reefs with their anchors and through sewage pollution, not to mention the fact that tourists chip off chunks of coral as souvenirs and local people do the same on a commercial scale for sale to passengers.

Even non-ocean-going cruises, such as those around the Galapagos Islands or in the Antarctic, can have a high carbon dioxide cost. A ship taking tourists around the Galapagos Islands is estimated to emit about a tonne of carbon dioxide per passenger over an eight-day cruise and an Antarctic ice-breaker uses a massive third of a tonne per day per passenger. And these figures do not include the emissions from the international flight to get to the departure port.

If you really want to experience a relaxing water-based cruise, the best alternative is a sail-based cruise such as on an Egyptian felucca along the Nile or on a Kenyan dhow but you will still be incurring the flight emissions.

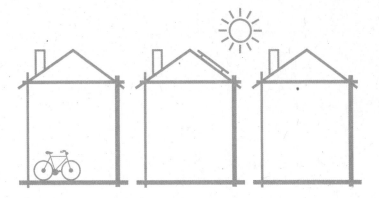

Home eco-audit

This section of the eco-audit walkabout is usually not very long, but if the household is a two-car family and each of those cars is driven the UK average of 8,700 miles a year, the combined emissions could be over 6.2 tonnes. This is more than the average house emits in an entire year for heat and lighting, so you will get a feel of how important it is. In addition, any long-distance flights taken could overshadow any savings made in home energy. Once you have filled in your eco-audit form, calculating your annual emissions from car use and any flights taken, you will have a good idea of where your emissions are excessive and how action can be taken to radically reduce them.

Driving

If you feel it is essential to have a car, then the most important thing is to choose the right one and to use it only when absolutely necessary. As we have already seen, the variation in emissions even within the same class of car is enormous, so make sure you check the government websites before coming to any decisions.

Many people cannot imagine coping without a car on the drive, but there are plenty of ways to provide transport without lashing out over £5,500 the RAC says it costs to run an average car for a year.

• Buy a bicycle for use on short journeys.

• If you have to go to the supermarket for a big shop, go by public transport, then get a taxi home. If the average fare to your house is £10, then the annual cost would be about £500, which is far cheaper than running a car just for shopping. Or better still, get an organic box scheme or supermarket to deliver your shopping to you.

• Place large baskets on your bicycle, so you do not have to lug the shopping home.

• Share the drive to work with others and slash your petrol costs.

• Join a car club and pay by the hour when you need, for example, to visit parents or carry heavy loads.

• If you really need a car for holidays, hire one for the period.

While the fundamental advice for eco-friendly transport is to walk, cycle and use public transport wherever possible, the following tips will be useful for those who are not yet ready to give up their car.

Tips to reduce your car emissions

1 Buy the smallest car possible in line with your requirements and then get the lowest-emitting car in that class. The smallest petrol-powered cars, such as the Citroën C1 (109g/km), and the diesel Volkswagen Polo BlueMotion (102g/km) have emissions almost as low as or lower than many of the expensive hybrid cars (see pages 229–30).

2 Use the car for essential journeys only.

3 Drive smoothly, not accelerating or braking too sharply, and changing gear at the right time. This can help cut up to 10 per cent of your fuel costs. If you drive a diesel car, try changing

up a gear when the rev counter reaches 2,000 rpm; for a petrol car change up at 2,500 rpm.

4 Take out all the heavy junk you are carrying around in the car: the heavier the car, the more fuel it uses.

5 Take off the roof rack if you use it only rarely: the extra drag increases fuel use.

6 Use a mixture of recycled bio-diesel if you have a diesel engine.

7 Observe the speed limit: driving over the speed limit uses more fuel.

8 Use air-conditioning only when absolutely essential: it increases fuel consumption by up to 20 per cent.

9 Fill up the tank when passing a filling station rather than making a special journey.

10 Check your route first to get you to your destination without wasting fuel.

11 Keep your tyres at the right pressure: soft tyres increase fuel use.

12 Keep the engine regularly maintained to ensure operating efficiency.

13 Turn off the engine if you are likely to be stopped for more than three minutes: idling wastes fuel and increases emissions unnecessarily.

Cycling

For the first time in decades, the numbers of people taking up cycling again in London are soaring. A combination of awareness about climate-change issues surrounding cars and the new congestion charge has led to a renaissance for the most efficient non-motorized machine on the planet. There are any number of good reasons why you should think seriously about taking up cycling.

• It can save a lot of money. If you take depreciation into account, the average cost of running a car can be over £3,500 a year. A decent bike will set you back about £300, with an extra annual maintenance cost of around £150. Buying a bike can cost 50 per cent less in the UK if your employer is signed up to the Cycle to Work scheme, which allows you to pay for the bike from your salary before income tax.

• If you like to exercise by going to the gym, replace your existing gym membership with cycling and save even more money. Gym memberships can vary from £30 to £100 per month, so the potential saving is between £360 and £1,200 a year.

• You can free up more leisure time by combining exercise with your commute.

• You will not have to pay road tax or any car-parking and congestion charges as bicycles are exempt.

• Repair costs are minimal in comparison with a car and you will be able to carry out a fair few of them yourself.

• It can reduce stress levels to know you are in charge of a vehicle that is not a potential killer.

• Cyclists are fitter than the majority of people who take no exercise, so they are less likely to get ill.

• Cycling does not strain the joints in the way that jogging on hard roads does. It also tones the legs, the back and the abdominal muscles.

• It can help keep your heart younger and healthier. The British Heart Foundation says that regular cyclists have the hearts of people ten years younger. Their heart rates are significantly lower than those of people who do not exercise. All of which means that cycling is a good way of avoiding a heart bypass!

• It can save you lots of time if you live in a city, as cycling means you never have to wait in a traffic jam again, or allow for bus breakdowns or signal failures on the way to work.

• You will not have to worry about finding a parking space, as you can nearly always lock up a bicycle near where you are going.

• You will be exposed to less pollution than car drivers, as pollution levels inside cars are higher than those breathed in by cyclists.

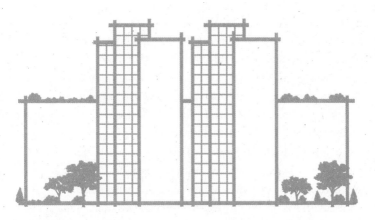

Work eco-audit

Transport issues vary widely from company to company, but one thing will be common to nearly all of them: staff have to travel to work. So one of your first questions should be whether a company travel plan exists. This is a plan that seeks to identify how staff travel to work and then ensures that as many of them as possible avoid using their own cars.

As the travel needs of almost every company will be different, depending on location and the needs of individual staff members, so every travel plan will need to take specific circumstances such as location and the availability of public transport into account. However, you could pick items out of the list below that might fit your particular company's circumstances.

In addition to asking about a travel plan, you will need to ascertain what transport is provided for staff and whether the company operates any trucks or vans. If they do have a transport fleet, then it is important that you talk to the fleet manager to find out if carbon emissions form a major part of the company's buying criteria and if the vehicles they have are the smallest suitable for the purpose. There is no point in having a mainly empty truck delivering individual loads when a small van would be more suitable. It is important also to ask if regular training in eco-driving methods is in place for company drivers and is available for newcomers as part of their induction process.

If they are running a diesel-powered fleet, it is worth mentioning that they should look for a source of reused vegetable oil diesel. This can be safely stored on site and mixed manually in the vehicles. A large London food supplier, Essex Flour and Grain, that I have eco-audited in the East End has done this and has been really happy with the results, which help them cut their carbon dioxide emissions for transport by over 30 per cent. As this was their largest source of emissions, it was really important to them.

Sat-nav and vehicle-tracking systems can also eliminate fuel being wasted when drivers are lost or will stop them using the vehicles without permission.

Work travel plan

- Find out how many staff are using personal motorized transport to come to work and monitor this every year for the annual eco-audit report.

- Establish a cycle loan scheme for staff, whereby staff can borrow the money to buy a bike but can pay back over the year interest-free. The UK government currently provides tax benefits for such schemes, further reducing the cost to staff.

- Establish a travel loan scheme if the company premises are served by local transport. As with the cycle loan scheme, this allows staff to borrow money to buy an annual season ticket, which is far cheaper than weekly or monthly passes.

- Provide safe, accessible cycle parking for staff where practical.

- If currently providing free parking spaces for staff, discuss with them if this could be phased out, maybe by providing other benefits in lieu, such as contributions towards season tickets.

- In larger companies there may be scope for providing a company bus to and from the nearest train station if it is not served by public transport.

- Where practical replace company cars with other benefits.

- Ensure those company cars that are necessary are the smallest size and have the lowest emissions compatible with business requirements.

- Provide staff training in eco-driving methods that reduce fuel consumption.
- Provide any essential company cars with satellite navigation.
- Where practical, introduce telephone- and video-conferencing to replace unnecessary travel, especially flight, for staff.
- Record the number of taxi journeys taken annually and make a guesstimate of how many tonnes of carbon dioxide are used.
- Start procedures to record litres of petrol or diesel used annually and convert into tonnes of carbon dioxide.
- Start procedures to record the number of flights taken annually and convert into tonnes of carbon dioxide.
- If staff make journeys locally, provide company bicycles or encourage them to use public transport (remember to provide company cycling insurance for these journeys). You could also paint the bicycles in the company logo for free local advertising.
- Encourage and facilitate car-sharing among employees.
- Introduce an employment policy whereby if two applicants are equally qualified, preference will be given to the one who does not have to use personal motorized transport to travel to work.
- Join an emergency breakdown organization that does not lobby for the motoring industry. The main one in the UK is the Environmental Transport Association (ETA).
- Seek to phase out payments for taxis for work purposes and replace with cycle or public transport allowances.

- For medium to long journeys encourage staff to use the train rather than cars or planes. The train to Paris produces about a tenth of the carbon dioxide emissions of a flight, with the added advantage that staff will be available by phone, will be able to work with a laptop in greater comfort and will arrive at their destination more rested.

As well as being a potential source of considerable carbon dioxide emissions, transport can be a heavy cost burden for many companies. Moreover, one of the most chilling statistics I came across when doing research for this book was that, according to the UK Health and Safety Executive, five times more employees die in road accidents than they do in the office or factory. It was for this reason that a UK national trade union recently adopted a union travel plan that has already reduced travel by 15 per cent. The motivation for them was not the environmental cost but simply that they wanted to reduce staff fatalities!

Vehicle fuels

What fuel a company chooses to use for its vehicles is a complex issue. Sometimes on an eco-audit walkabout, clients ask me what is the greenest fuel. To be perfectly frank, I find this a hard question to answer, as nearly all the fuels have pluses and minuses. While modern transport has made a significant contribution to our quality of life, its overuse is threatening climate catastrophe. So really any advice on what fuel to use should be prefaced with advice on how important it is that total transport kilometres be reduced in the first place, if at all practical for the business, and any vehicle used should be the smallest and most efficient for the purpose required. Many tips to achieve this are listed in the suggestions for a work travel plan, but in the real world most companies and individuals are not going to be willing or able to give up using motorized transport. You will therefore need to know about the different means of powering that transport.

Electricity

Electric vehicles have some of the lowest carbon dioxide emissions of any on the road. The G-Wiz electric car emits about 35 grams per kilometre, compared to 102 grams for what is currently the lowest-emitting diesel car (Volkswagen Polo BlueMotion). In addition, it has zero emissions of all pollutants from the car itself, as the carbon dioxide is emitted at the power station and not from the vehicle. The main drawback is the limited range on one charge – usually about 65–100 kilometres – so they are only really suitable for urban or short journeys, but that would be fine for most commutes.

If charged with renewable electricity, they would have zero carbon dioxide emissions, but as there is not enough renewable energy to replace the current mains electricity sourced from fossil fuels, a wholesale switch to electric vehicles currently would not be practical. However, if a company was able to invest in, for example, a large commercial wind turbine, then they might have enough excess electricity to fuel their transport needs. This could also apply to a rural farm or domestic premises, which might also be able to generate excess electricity from micro-hydro.

For companies with urban delivery routes, electric vehicles might have a role to play. While electric trucks can still be expensive to buy, the fuel costs are about a fifth of those of a diesel truck. There are now some electric 7.5-tonne vehicles that can travel up to 210 kilometres on one charge. Tesco and Marks & Spencer are beginning to use such electric vehicles.

Petrol

Petrol is obviously a fossil fuel and its use is a significant contributor to the climate crisis. However, it is worth noting that the most efficient petrol engines can have far lower emissions than luxury hybrid engines (see page 230).

Diesel

Diesel is another fossil fuel made from oil, but diesel engines are more efficient than petrol engines and produce up to 30 per cent less carbon dioxide emissions than equivalent petrol engines. They do emit more particulates and other pollutants, but in my view, as the current climate crisis is so serious, I would definitely advise a diesel engine over a petrol engine if there is a choice.

Vegetable oil

Many diesel engines can take the addition of vegetable oil to fossil-fuel derived diesel in mixtures of up to 30 per cent without any need for any adaptation to the vehicle. With an adaptation to the engine, the engine can take up to 100 per cent vegetable oil. Indeed, the original engine produced in 1895 by Dr Rudolf Diesel was initially designed to run on peanut oil. He predicted then that vegetable oil would in time become as important as petroleum, but I am not sure he realized how long it might take for that to come true! Higher percentages of vegetable oil can be problematic in winter cold spells, which is why adaptation is needed for such high mixtures.

In principle, vegetable oil is carbon neutral in that the carbon dioxide released is simply what has been stored during the growth of the plants, thus crucially avoiding the release of the carbon dioxide stored in fossil fuels. However, the serious issue for vegetable oil is how it is sourced and how much fossil fuel is burned in its production. If tropical forests were cleared to make way for more palm oil plantations for bio-diesels, then there would be both an ecological disaster, with the loss of irreplaceable virgin forests and their species, and a net increase in carbon dioxide emissions, as the millions of tonnes locked up in the virgin forests were released. Such a release of carbon dioxide from virgin tropical forests is one of the largest current sources of emissions worldwide. Indeed, non-industrialized Indonesia was the third highest national source of carbon dioxide emissions in 2006 due to the illegal burning of its virgin forests.

On the other side of this debate about bio-diesels, it should be remembered that over 70 per cent of agricultural land in the US and UK is devoted not to food crops for humans but rather to livestock rearing, which is an incredibly wasteful use of the land. If we reduced our wasteful meat eating, some land could be redirected to vegetable oil production.

Installing a conversion kit so a diesel engine will run on pure vegetable oil costs between £450 and £1,200. At about 45p per litre for the cheapest vegetable oil, this is clearly competitive, except that the UK Chancellor recently doubled the excise duty payable on such vegetable oils, thus wiping out the financial benefit. In Germany it is zero-rated.

Recycled vegetable oil

If you can get it, filtered reused vegetable cooking oil from restaurants, is probably one of the greenest fuels available because it is a recycled product. As we have already seen, this means it has not had to be dumped in a landfill site, where it can contribute to the production of methane, and also it cannot be blamed for an increase in rainforest destruction or have to bear the fossil-fuel costs associated with growing vegetable oil from scratch.

Bio-diesel

As mentioned above, this is produced from transesterificated vegetable oil and can be used in most diesel engines up to a 30 per cent mix without any modification. It has much the same environmental pros and cons as vegetable oil, but by some strange UK Treasury quirk it does qualify for a reduction in petrol duties, whereas non-de-esterified vegetable oil does not.

There are of course some carbon dioxide emissions from the fuel used for processing, but there is no reason why the energy cannot be supplied by renewables.

Bio-ethanol

Bio-ethanol is to petrol what bio-diesel is to diesel – an alcohol produced from plants that can be used in low-percentage mixtures in petrol engines. A 5 per cent mix is already becoming standard in countries across the EU. However, to use high percentages of bio-ethanol, such as E85, which is an 85 per cent mix of ethanol to petrol, the engine has to be specially adapted. Some motor manufacturers, such as Saab and Ford, are beginning to produce cars that will take any mix of ethanol and petrol up to 85 per cent.

Some countries – Brazil, for example – are already providing more than 40 per cent of their transport fuels from ethanol produced by fermenting sugar cane. There are claims that this has added to pressure on Amazon deforestation and the carbon dioxide emissions from this exceed the emissions saved. However, research is now taking place on what are called second-generation bio-ethanol facilities that can produce ethanol from the cellulose of all waste agricultural materials. Experimental plants are already up and running in Denmark. Should these experiments prove successful, such bio-ethanol could be a valuable green fuel in the future, as fuel could be made from such materials as the waste straw after harvesting.

Hybrids

Hybrids are cars that have an electric engine in addition to a petrol engine. The batteries for the electric engine are charged up when the car is braking. Unlike electric cars, they do not need to be charged up by plugging them into an electric socket, but some manufacturers are looking at models that can also be plugged in. The cars can run solely on the electric engine when travelling at slow speeds in urban areas. The best-known example, the Toyota Prius, has an emissions rating of 104 grams per kilometre, which is the lowest of any fossil-fuel-powered car on the market. However, the emissions recorded in test-drive situations have not always been replicated on the road.

That said, *Which?* magazine found the Lexus 4x4 Hybrid to be 27 per cent , the Toyota Prius 44 per cent and the Honda Civic Hybrid 19 per cent greener than their petrol equivalents. Such cars make sense if you have to have a bigger car than the best of the petrol- or diesel-powered smaller cars.

LPG

Liquefied Petroleum Gas is a by-product of the petrochemical industry and so is a fossil fuel, but again it emits up to 30 per cent less carbon dioxide than petrol and so is a distinctly greener fuel. Cars running on LPG are normally hybrids also using petrol. There are very few LPG stations in the UK at present. However, the corporate events company MotivAction in Stevenage, to take one example, has switched its fleet to LPG, with a refilling station on site.

CNG

Compressed Natural Gas is another fossil fuel (methane) and so is not renewable, but its use results in up to 30 per cent less carbon dioxide emissions than petrol and so it has a significant environmental advantage. There are currently only nine CNG filling stations within the UK, which are generally strategically located near motorways, but more are planned.

Bio-gas

Bio-gas is the methane gas harvested from the gas released during the decay of natural products such as sewage or rotting plants and animals. It is one of the greenest fuels as it does not require much energy to process and, if allowed to escape unburned, methane is a powerful contributor to the climate crisis as mentioned before. Whilst measured over a century it is estimated to be over 22 times a more powerful climate crisis gas than CO2. If measured over a decade, due to its short life span, some scientists estimate it to be up to 100 times more powerful. Thus anything we can do to reduce its release is really important. A number of Scandinavian countries have developed buses and trains that can run on this fuel, but it is not generally available commercially yet.

Hydrogen

Some hydrogen-powered vehicles are now being produced on an experimental basis. The main drawback is that the hydrogen is made from water, using electrolysis to split the H_2O molecule into hydrogen and oxygen, and so requires large amounts of electricity. Until there is an excess of renewable electricity, this does not currently provide a solution to reducing carbon dioxide emissions. The other disadvantages are that it requires tanks four times bigger than a petrol tank and there are safety issues concerning ventilation. However in countries like Iceland with huge potential for geo-thermal energy, which can be harnessed for the production of hydrogen, it really makes sense to switch to a hydrogen economy, which excitingly has been official Icelandic government policy since 2002. It aims to be a totally fossil-fuel-free economy by 2030.

Chapter 10

Eco-friendly shopping

Eco-shopping

In addition to our choices and use of energy and transport, one of the greatest ways we will affect the environment is what and how much we buy and consume. From food and furniture to clothes and bathroom supplies, everything we buy comes with a carbon and environmental cost, as well as a financial one. The same is true for the supplies and raw materials a company buys. It is therefore crucial that you include what and how a household or company goes about its buying in your eco-audit. The good thing is that anyone interested in eco-auditing has probably already started buying in a more eco-friendly manner. The more you know about eco-friendly spending, the better equipped you will be to help them along the way.

The Co-operative Bank estimated that in 2005 over £30 billion was spent in the UK on ethically branded products, an increase of 11 per cent over the previous year. This was more than what was spent on tobacco and beer combined, but the fact that it now represents just over 5 per cent of total household spending shows how far there is to go. Ideally, of course the top priority is to eliminate unnecessary consumer spending in the first place and to direct money instead into non-environmentally destructive activities and products. But no matter how much consumer spending is reduced there will always be a need to shop or for a company to purchase supplies. This chapter covers the items purchased for a home and business that have not been covered already and deals with some of the overarching approaches to shopping that will promote eco-friendliness.

Organic food

Organic farming means that farmers grow their crops without the use of artificial chemical fertilizers and pesticides. To be certified as an organic farm they must farm in a way that supports rather than destroys local wildlife and they must treat their livestock in a humane way and without the indiscriminate use of antibiotics. This involves extra costs and labour, but means a healthier countryside and healthier food. A recent study by the Harvard School of Public Health found that those regularly exposed to pesticides had a 70 per cent higher incidence of Parkinson's disease. Despite this, over 31,000 tons of pesticides are sprayed on UK farms and gardens every year. Cereal crops are sprayed five times, potatoes up to 12 times and apples up to 18 times a year. In addition, some scientists blame the factory farming of chickens for the development and spread of avian flu. This is because the huge flocks of birds caged unnaturally on top of each other indoors provide the perfect breeding ground for the development of highly contagious viruses.

Organic food sales are soaring in the UK, with over £1.6 billion worth sold in 2006. The news gets even better with baby food, where almost half of total sales in the UK are now organic.

Reasons to buy organic food

■ Over 400 different chemicals are used on UK farms every year.

■ 4.5 billion litres of pesticides are sprayed on UK farms each year according to the Soil Association.

■ It costs over £120 million just in running costs for the UK water companies to remove these pesticides each year, in addition to the billions in infrastructure they have had to invest over the last 15 years to remove them.

■ Buying organic food, which is certified GM-free, means you avoid the risk of eating, or helping to fund the planting of, genetically modified crops, with all the inherent threats to the environment and future crop security and prosperity for small farmers.

- Organic farming nurtures the soil for future generations, whereas factory farming results in disastrous loss of topsoil, with millions of tonnes being blown away from the huge, hedgeless mono-crop fields.

- Through the avoidance of pesticides and other harmful practices, organic farming helps to protect rural wildlife, wild flowers and plants.

- Organic farming eliminates the health risks for both farm-workers and consumers associated with food sprayed with artificial chemicals.

- Organic farming reduces the pollution of rivers and waterways with artificial chemicals and fertilizers. Nitrogen fertilizers from intensive farming form one of the biggest threats to healthy waterways.

- Organic farming requires the humane treatment of animals, with intensive factory farming banned.

- Organic farming helps to restore beauty and variety to the countryside, preserving habitats for wildlife and wild flowers for the next generation.

Local food/food miles

The concept of food miles involves calculating how many miles an item of food has travelled from where it was grown to where it is eaten. This is important because transport is responsible for approximately 27 per cent of total global carbon dioxide emissions and food makes up about 40 per cent of total road freight tonnage. The Department of the Environment estimates that UK food transport results annually in the emission of over 19 million tonnes of carbon dioxide. A kilogram of apples from a local organic box scheme will result in about 10 grams of carbon dioxide being released, while a kilogram from New Zealand will result in over 300 grams. Air-freighted fruit and vegetables are the real villains of the piece, making up 13 per cent of all air freight. Vegetables flown in from Africa can use up to 33 times the emissions of locally produced vegetables that are not grown in fossil-fuelled greenhouses. The MEP Caroline Lucas did some research and found that the average UK Christmas dinner clocks up a whopping 30,000 food miles.

Sustainable Energy Action in London estimate that about a third of our carbon emissions come from our consumption of food. The figure is this high because of the energy used for growing or raising the crops or animals, the processing of the food, its transport, its cooking in the home and finally the disposal of the leftovers, plus the methane food waste emits if dumped in landfill. It is important to buy as much food as possible from local, organic and unprocessed sources.

Meat consumption

While researching for this book I stumbled upon an amazing fact in a 2003 report by climate consultant Jean-Marc Jancovici, which stated that a kilogram of unprocessed meat resulted in the release of 10 kilograms of carbon dioxide. The average meat consumption per person per year is about 80 kilograms in the UK. Imported meat from South America costs about another 25 per cent in transport emissions on top of this. Thus a family of four could be releasing up to a whopping 4 tonnes of carbon dioxide from their meat eating alone in one year. This is over half of the average household emissions for all energy used for space heating and electricity!

Comparing emissions

Meat	Kg CO_2 per kg meat produced
Veal	40
Beef	10
Pork	3
Chicken	2

Reasons to reduce meat and dairy intake

- A reduced-meat or vegetarian diet results in far lower CO_2 emissions. The University of Chicago estimates that a meat diet emits over 1.5 tonnes more greenhouse gases than a vegetable-based diet.

- The UN states that livestock (mainly our 1.5 billion cows) produce a whopping 18 per cent of global climate change gases (mainly methane).

- The UN states that the clearing of forests for cattle ranching and feed production is one of the biggest drivers of rainforest destruction worldwide (e.g. over 70 per cent of the cleared Amazon rainforest).

- Overgrazing by cows is turning a fifth of all pastures and ranges worldwide into desert.

- Livestock emit over two-thirds of the world's ammonia, one of the biggest causes of acid rain.

- Livestock rearing takes up over 70 per cent of all agricultural land.

- Over 650 million tonnes of grain is fed to livestock every year worldwide; in industrial countries that is over 70 per cent of grain.

- The same amount of land that provides enough meat protein for one person will provide enough soya protein for 30 people.

- It takes over 100,000 litres of water to produce just 1 kilogram of beef.

- It takes 1,000 litres of water to produce 1 litre of milk.

- Over-production of meat is contributing to the loss of precious topsoil, more than 85 per cent of which is attributed to livestock rearing. The US has lost more than 50 per cent of its topsoil since 1960, according to the *Ecologist* magazine. This is 17 times faster than nature can replace it.

- The grain used to feed the US beef herd would feed the population of India and China combined.

These facts become starker when you realize that in six of the last seven years, global human consumption of food has exceeded global food production. In other words, we have been eating into our food stockpiles for six of the last seven years. According to the US Department of Agriculture, there was a shortfall of over 50 million tonnes in 2006. The planet's food stocks, which were at 115 days of reserves eight years ago, are now at about 60 days. Some 16,000 children a day are dying of starvation, while over a third of our harvests goes to feed livestock for the rich. So encouraging people to eat less meat, while not part of a usual eco-audit, is nevertheless something that needs to be thought about very seriously if we want to radically reduce our environmental footprint.

Ethical fish

Surely one of the stupidest things a species can do is to hunt the creatures it eats to extinction. Yet that is what humanity appears to be doing with fish. One of the world's richest fishing fields off the coast of Newfoundland was so over-fished in the last century that it eventually completely collapsed. The amount of fish taken from the seas to feed rapidly rising human populations has soared from 18 to 95 million tonnes since 1957. The UN estimates that 17 per cent of commercial fish species are now over-exploited.

In addition, hidden behind these figures is a story of unnecessary cruelty and destruction. Factory-sized fishing boats now trawl nets as big as football pitches across the ocean floor, destroying the seabed and scooping up almost everything that lives. Millions of tonnes of fish are thrown back into the sea after they have died as they cannot be commercially eaten. This includes thousands of dolphins, whales, porpoises, walruses and endangered turtles who have been cruelly trapped in the nets.

Some fisheries, however, are managed in such a way that the fish stocks are nurtured rather than destroyed. The Marine Stewardship Council (MSC) does the same job for fish as the Forest Stewardship Council does for timber products. If you are concerned about such matters, check their website to see what kind of fish can be eaten ethically without worrying about contributing to over-exploitation. The Marine Conservation Society website offers information on issues affecting over 120 fish species and also produces a pocket-sized *Good Fish Guide*.

Fish farming

Originally seen as a way of avoiding the need to catch wild fish, fish farming has turned into an environmental disaster because restricting wild fish that naturally swim in the ocean to tiny crowded cages results in a high incidence of disease. This in turn leads to high concentrations of antibiotics being poured into their cages and the unnaturally high concentration of fish droppings also pollutes the seas where the cages are situated. These diseases are now spreading to the wild fish populations, with disastrous consequences.

In addition salmon, which are carnivores, have to be fed large amounts of fish caught elsewhere to keep them alive. Salmon fish farming in Scotland has exploded from 800 tonnes a year in 1980 to over 150,000 tonnes today. The World Watch Institute estimates that each tonne of salmon requires 5 tonnes of fish to feed them, which means that over three-quarters of a million tonnes of harvested fish are now being fed to the salmon in Scotland alone.

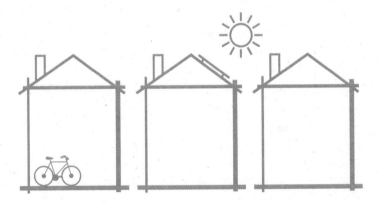

Home eco-audit

According to one study, food production accounts for about 17 per cent of total UK carbon dioxide emissions. So looking at what food you buy is probably the best place to start in a home shopping eco-audit walkabout. The first thing to consider is joining a local organic box scheme. This will really help to support more eco-friendly agriculture and at the same time reduce food miles – both the producer's and yours. You will not have to make a supermarket trip as the produce is brought direct to your door, and since the box scheme will cover other homes in the area overall mileage will decrease. This is important when you realize that UK consumers now drive 22 kilometres a week on average for shopping, a figure that has gone up over 50 per cent in the last 20 years with the closure of local shops in the face of supermarket competition. Aim to use local organic suppliers as much as possible and check out nearby farmers' markets.

Buying in-season fruit and vegetables from a farmers' market is a guarantee that your produce has not been draining precious water resources in countries such as Kenya and Spain. So much water is used to irrigate strawberries to supply them in winter for the north European and UK market that the water table in the Spanish strawberry-growing region has dropped by over 50 per cent. The main river in the region, the Rocina, is now dry between July and October, where before it ran all the year round. This is now threatening to dry out one of Europe's most important water-fowl wetlands. Many imported Spanish tomatoes have also been grown with water from desalination plants, which require large amounts of fossil fuel to run them and also result in increased coastal salinity, when the extremely salty water that has been extracted is released. This can be damaging for aquatic wildlife.

Make sure that everyone in the household knows about MSC fish and FSC wood, and why it is so important that only such certified products are bought. Think about the advantages of buying second-hand or even antique furniture, and obviously also energy-efficient goods. Go to local architectural salvage yards if you are building or refurbishing, and use the Internet for a range of goods – some free (check out Freecycle), some auctioned (eBay). Freecycle has the advantage over eBay in that it is organized locally, eliminating the need for long journeys.

Make sure you are using recycled paper products in the kitchen and bathroom, and choose organic cosmetics. Try to buy organic cotton clothing, which avoids the massive use of pesticides required for mass production of cotton. Organic bamboo and hemp are even more eco-friendly as they use far less water than is used for growing cotton. Local charity shops are a great place to find good clothes. It is worth emphasizing the cost of clothes that are never worn. Churchill Home Insurance research found that the average UK female buys over £12,000 worth of clothing in their lifetime that they never actually wear! Men were only a little less likely to impulse-buy, their average spend being £8,000.

If you are buying new furniture, household items and toys , make sure they are made from sustainable materials like FSC-certified wood. Over 60 million indigenous people live in rainforests across the globe. Buying illegal timber such as mahogany results in the destruction of their homes and death or destitution for those who lived there. Rooms full of broken plastic toys mean litres of wasted oil going to landfill sooner or later.

Tips for eco-clothes shopping

1 **Reduce the amount of new clothes bought.**

2 **Buy antique or second-hand clothes.**

3 **Avoid purchasing clothes made from artificial materials, such as polyester, which require huge amounts of water in their manufacture and dyes that have to be used at very high temperatures.**

4 Buy fair-trade organic cotton or hemp clothing.

5 Buy coloured clothes that can be washed at 30°C rather than predominantly white clothing that requires higher temperatures.

6 Avoid buying clothes that need to be dry-cleaned in toxic chemicals.

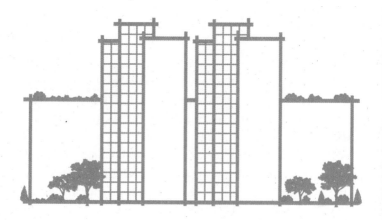

Work eco-audit

Like all aspects of an eco-audit, the supplier walkabout will vary widely from company to company. If yours is an office-based company, the main areas to consider will probably be stationery supplies, printed materials, cleaning supplies (dealt with in Chapter 6) and catering. If you go through the stationery cupboard or store during the walkabout, you will see whether your company is buying recycled paper and other stationery products. The largest item in most offices will be photocopying paper. Despite moves towards the so-called paperless office, most businesses still use enormous amounts of paper. It is amazing how many businesses that have all their photocopiers and printers set to single-sided printing. Having carried out an eco-audit for Merton Volunteer Services Council, I advised them to reset their printers to print double-sided automatically and they found to their delight that paper use went down by over 46 per cent almost immediately.

Equally surprising to me as I eco-audit businesses is how many of them do not buy recycled paper, even though they recycle their own office paper. Over 80 per cent of people in the UK now recycle at least one thing a week, but only 10 per cent actually buy recycled products. The problem with this is that if we do not buy recycled products, the huge mountains of collected materials will have to be exported abroad to be processed. While this is better than seeing it dumped into landfill sites, the ideal would be if all businesses closed the recycling loop and bought the full range of recycled paper products. It is now possible even to get pens and pencils made from recycled materials.

The stationery cupboard will also usually contain a stock of headed notepaper, compliment slips and business cards. Check whether these are on recycled paper or not. When recycled paper first came on to the market about 15 years ago, it was often quite 'dusty' and so not very suitable for use in photocopiers. The quality has improved a lot since then and can now compete with the best non-recycled papers. Unfortunately, not everyone responsible for paper purchasing is aware of this, so you should let them know. When recommending the switch to recycled paper, suggest that the fact the company is printing on recycled paper be included in the artwork. Doing the right thing is one thing, but it is also important to be seen to be doing so, thus spreading the word that recycled paper is the accepted ethical norm for businesses.

In the staff kitchen, look out for disposables – paper plates, plastic cups, cutlery – and see if coffee and sugar sachets instead of sugar shakers and loose coffee granules are being used. Ideally all teas and coffee provided should be organic and fair-trade. While not strictly an environmental issue, it is good for a company's integrity to be buying products that are not based on the exploitation of people in developing countries. Check also whether the milk is organic and in returnable bottles.

At some point during the walkabout you will probably come across externally commissioned printed items, such as marketing and promotional materials or the annual company report. This can be one of the largest purchases of paper for many companies and so it is crucial that you have a talk with the person responsible, in order to discuss using recycled paper and possibly even vegetable inks. Many people will be delighted to have these issues raised and will be eager for advice.

If your company buys a significant number of products direct from a manufacturer, this provides opportunities to negotiate with the manufacturer on ways to make production more eco-friendly. For example, you could ask for the products to be delivered in returnable packaging or you could look at having the product made from more recyclable and eco-friendly materials, or from locally sourced materials using less energy.

Questions to ask the company

■ Do you really need to buy a particular product in the first place?

■ Are there ways to reduce the number of products needed by reducing waste or adopting better work practices?

■ Are all paper products bought made from recycled paper?

■ How much food and drink used by staff and catered events is made from local and organic produce, and if fish is provided is it MSC-certified?

■ Do you have an eco-friendly purchasing policy in place, based on reduce, reuse and recycle?

■ Do you buy reused furniture or other items?

■ Do you use organic paints?

■ Do you ask suppliers if they have an environmental policy and, if so, is it independently monitored annually?

■ If you buy new wood products, are they FSC-certified?

■ Do you use disposable products that could be replaced by reusables?

■ Are all those authorized to make purchases on behalf of the company trained in eco-friendly purchasing policies?

Questions to ask the company's suppliers

- Do they have an environmental policy in place? Ask to see an electronic copy.

- Do they have regular external eco- or environmental audits carried out? Ask to see evidence of environmental policy outcomes being measured annually.

- Do they use a green electricity supplier or provide any of their own eco-electricity?

- Do they try and use recycled raw materials or products?

- Do they use returnable packaging?

- Do they have a green purchasing policy? Ask to see evidence that it is being followed.

- Do they have a waste reduction and recycling policy? Ask to see evidence that it is being followed.

- Do they have a local purchasing policy? Ask to see evidence that it is being followed.

- If they use wood, is it FSC-certified?

- If they produce food products or consume food on the premises, do they purchase organic or locally produced food, plus MSC-certified fish if relevant?

- Do they measure their energy carbon footprint and have they reduced it successfully?

- What grades did their buildings achieve for the energy performance certificates?

Chapter 11

My eco-lifestyle

How I've made my life more eco-friendly

When I stand in front of audiences asking them to take action to cut their environmental and carbon footprints, I think it is crucial that I have taken steps to tackle my own. From the beginning Mahatma Gandhi's maxim to be the change one wants to see in the world has underpinned all of my political and environmental campaigning. As I mentioned in the introduction, this applies to you too, whether you want to be a volunteer or professional eco-auditor. In relation to making my own life more eco-friendly, I translate Gandhi's maxim into asking myself, no matter what I am doing, whether I can do it in a way that is less damaging to the environment, with the time, knowledge and money I have at my disposal. This is also my approach to the homes and companies that I eco-audit.

As I started writing this final chapter, coincidentally my annual eco-data day arrived. I wrote down all the meter readings for my home's environmental performance on 24 June last year. The last time I had recorded my home's environmental footprint, it was responsible for emitting half a tonne of carbon dioxide, which compares well with the national average of 6 tonnes. I was hoping this year that the figures would show that on energy I had finally managed to make my home carbon neutral – in other words, that the green energy produced and exported would exceed any fossil fuels the house had imported.

The figures gave the following results:

Gas consumption
609 kWh = 116 kg CO_2
UK average: 33,500 kWh per home

Exported electricity
598 kWh = 257 kg CO_2
UK average: statistically zero

Imported electricity
384 kWh
UK average: 5,200 kWh

Net exported electricity
214 kWh
UK average: statistically zero

As the imported electricity was bought from the domestic renewable-electricity supplier Good Energy, who get all their electricity from non-fossil sources such as hydro, solar and wind, the carbon dioxide for this is taken as zero. So, as the only fuels I consume in the house are electricity and gas, to calculate the annual energy carbon footprint for the house, I need to take the weight of carbon dioxide for gas imported from the carbon dioxide equivalent for the exported electricity.

Net home energy carbon footprint
116 kg (imported gas) – 257 kg (exported electricity)
    = –141 kg CO_2
UK average: 6 tonnes or 6,000 kg CO_2 per year

When I did the figures I whooped with delight. After 15 years of learning and practising how to reduce my home's energy carbon footprint, I had made it not only carbon neutral but 'climate-positive' – or in other words carbon negative. This means that the eco-electricity I had exported from the solar panels on the roof to the national grid had exceeded in carbon dioxide equivalent terms the fossil-fuel gas I had imported into my home for heating and cooking. I cannot guarantee it, but to my knowledge this is, if not the first, definitely one of the very first homes in London to reach this exciting milestone. All we need to do now is get all the other 20 million UK homes to do the same as quickly as possible!

The other figures for my home's environmental consumption from June 2006 to June 2007 were:

Mains water

9.88 cubic metres = 9,880 litres = 27 litres per day
London average: 160 litres of mains water per person per day

Waste

Domestic waste: 0.5 wheelie bins
Builders' waste: 3 black bin-bags
Imported waste wood: 32 wheelie bins
Net imported waste: 28.5 wheelie bins

Thus instead of contributing to the national waste mountain, my home actually helped reduce it!

Electricity

The results on electricity were achieved through a host of factors. I have changed all the light bulbs in my two-bedroom house over to energy-saving bulbs and LEDs. Thus the total wattage, if all the lights are turned on, currently comes to about 180 watts – which, considering I have eco-audited homes with 13,000 watts of lighting, is pretty efficient. In addition, my Earth Summit Pledge kicks in every time I leave a room and so the lights get turned off in rooms I am not using. I have an energy-efficient washing machine and a small energy-efficient fridge, which is turned down to minimum – it does not store any meat, as I am vegetarian. My clothes dry naturally in the sun in summer and by the fire in winter. I have a laptop instead of a PC and it has a 1-watt LED lamp that connects via a USB socket. This means that when I spend hours on my computer at night, I am using only 1 watt's worth of lighting in the whole house. I am fairly good at turning off any stand-by controls, but this has been made easier for the hard-to-get-at plug in the cupboard by the recent acquisition of a Stand-by Buster, which flicks it off via a remote-control handset. I do not have a TV. This is not to be eco-friendly, but because I am addicted to watching news programmes and the only way to stop was not to have one!

Having reduced electricity consumption, I then started looking at how I could provide for my remaining electricity needs in an eco-friendly manner and invested in a solar electric photovoltaic system in 1997. Mine was the first home in London to negotiate a contract with a national grid electricity company (EDF Energy) for them to buy metered solar electricity from a domestic home. During the day, if the solar panels produce more electricity than the house consumes (and in summer this can be over four times more), it gets exported out of the house into the national grid. Once a year I take a meter reading and send a modest bill to the electricity company, for the electricity they have bought from me. The electricity that I import at night and during the winter is bought from the eco-friendly electricity company Good Energy, which eliminates my imported carbon footprint for electricity.

Mine was also the first home in London to get planning permission for the installation of a domestic wind turbine in 2003. It was installed in 2006 but in the last six months it has produced only 12 kWh, which is a tiny amount and does not justify the £3,000 investment. But if no one experiments, we will never find out what works and what does not work; maybe one day the technology will improve to such an extent that the technology becomes feasible. It also means I can advise my clients from a position of real if not very positive experience!

Heating

In the vast majority of homes, almost three times more carbon dioxide is released in heating the home using oil or gas than in electricity consumption. Cutting down on the amount of heat needed was therefore an important first task for me. I did this most dramatically by only heating the rooms I was in and closing the doors of unoccupied rooms. I doubled the level of loft insulation by installing a layer of Warmcel insulation on top of the existing mineral wool. Over half the house now has double glazing, with the latest two windows being retro-fitted, thus saving the existing wooden frames. Windows, floors and doors have also been draught-proofed.

I replaced the criminally wasteful coal-effect gas fire in the living room with a flueless gas fire which is 100 per cent efficient, and as the flue had to be sealed, it meant I also cut down on heat lost through the fireplace even when the gas fire was not on. Since I installed my wood-burner, this acts as a useful back-up heating system, but prior to that there was a problem with condensation. Flueless gas fires are really only suitable for homes with existing central heating, the drying effect of which counteracts condensation from the flueless gas fire. If engineers could resolve this problem, flueless gas fires would have a larger role to play in energy efficiency.

But the most successful thing I did to reduce my remaining emissions for space heating to almost zero was to install the wood-burner. High-temperature wood-burners are allowed under the smokeless-zone regulations in urban Britain. Many people think that burning wood is the equivalent of burning fossil fuels, but surprisingly it is not. It releases the carbon dioxide stored from the atmosphere during the tree's growth rather than fossil-fuel carbon dioxide, which is the main cause of climate change. As long as replacement trees are planted, this is a renewable source of energy. (If they are not, obviously wood-burning becomes a problem.)

However, the wood that I burn does not even have to be delivered to my home. Last winter, I collected waste wood within a couple of hundred metres of my home in central London. There is a local plumber's merchant near my newsagent's that used to pay someone to collect their leftover wooden pallets by van and take them to the dump. They now allow me to collect them on my way back from buying my daily paper. Skips outside homes that are being refurbished are another rich source of lovely untreated wood. In addition to providing me with a carbon-neutral source of heat, it also gives me some fresh air and exercise when I go out into the yard to cut the timber and it provides a lovely cosy heart to my home in winter. The purchase of a simple Ecofan means that the heat from the wood-burner gets gently blown around the house rather than being concentrated around the fireplace.

Water heating

The third major source of my home's carbon emissions was the gas used for water heating. I reduced my hot-water needs by alternating a shower with a quick rinse at the sink every second day. I only shower for as long as it takes to clean me, rather than as a source of hot-water massage, as so many people seem to think it is and turn down the flow so it wets me rather than drowns me. I also wash the dishes every second day to cut down on the hot water required. The washing machine gets used only when I have enough laundry to fill it and for coloureds it is set at 30°C. I generally change my clothes every second day, rather than every day. To cover the hot water that I still use, I installed a solar hot-water panel two years ago and have been really pleased with the results. It provides over 70 per cent of my hot-water needs. I did not have to turn on the electric immersion back-up system last autumn until the end of October. And this year all my hot water for the washing machine, dish washing and showering since the beginning of April has come from the solar panels, as spring arrived very early. In winter the wood-burner boils water for shaving, washing and dishes quite nicely, but I did not install a back-burner, so it means simply putting a kettle on top.

Water supply

I have not got my mains water use down to zero yet but my daily use of 27 litres is now well below that of the average Londoner, who uses 160 litres per day. I feel strongly that mains water is a precious resource and so try to live a low-water lifestyle. Alternating showering and a sink wash, together with my other ways of reducing hot-water usage, reduces not only energy use but also water use. I have almost never used mains water to water the grass in summer, generally successfully relying on the water butt and water from the shower to get through any dry spells. A half-mug of water is plenty for washing my teeth and I never leave the tap running when washing vegetables or rinsing the dishes. My washing machine is a low-water as well as a low-energy model, which also helps. There are three filled plastic bottles in the WC cistern, reducing its capacity by about 1.5 litres, and there is also a retro-fitted Interflush device, which cuts the water off when released, meaning you use only 2 litres for a pee, although during the day I usually let it mellow, but not overnight as it stains the loo!

Having reduced my water requirements, I also provide a significant amount of what I need through the rain barrel attached to the downpipe from the kitchen roof and a rain harvester that collects water from the main roof. I was lucky that the layout of my house means the rain harvester can sit on top of the flat bathroom roof, thus providing water through a 2-metre pipe to the WC below it and a tap beside it for non-drinking purposes, without the need for any pump. The rain harvester normally provides over 70 per cent of my toilet requirements over a year. This year, however, as it has been almost continuously wet, I have not had to revert to the mains even once for the toilet, even though it is already August. Frequency of rain is more important than the amount of rain, as my storage capacity is limited. To cut the 28 litres a day even further, I am currently investigating whether it is possible to install another rain harvester by the kitchen, to be plumbed into the washing machine and hot-water cylinder. Watch this space!

Waste

I have long lived a low-waste lifestyle and am almost 100 per cent supermarket-free in my food shopping. I still chuckle when I remember refusing delivery of my new wheelie bin over ten years ago. The local council delivery men could not understand that I had no need for it, as I produced so little unrecyclable waste. They pushed it in and I pushed it out, over and over, until they gave up and took it away. It was a comedy scene straight out of a pantomime. I have since measured how much waste I produce in a year and found it was just over half a wheelie bin, or about a shopping bag every two months. I obviously recycle everything I can: cans, bottles, paper, cardboard, plastic bottles, clothes, shoes, etc. I have also had a composter for over 12 years that has taken all my garden and kitchen waste, reducing my waste by about a third and providing lovely compost in which to grow my tomatoes every year.

My organic fruit and vegetables get delivered by a local not-for-profit organic box scheme, which takes back their bags and any others I may have acquired for reuse. I use a cloth shopping bag, which eliminates most plastic bags, and I have a local cooperative food store near me at Elephant and Castle, which has a load of dried goods available loose, so you can bring your own refill bags. The empty honey jars and egg holders go back to local producers. I use cloth handkerchiefs, real soap instead of bottled chemical versions and have a toothbrush with a replaceable head. I also reduce the waste mountain by trying to buy second-hand goods where practical. Thus a lot of my clothes are from an Aids charity shop in Pimlico (the Crusaid Shop). All the furniture in my house is reused and I usually try and get other things I need from sites like eBay or Freecycle. All my lovely new bathroom wood flooring came from a guy on Freecycle in Vauxhall who had gutted his kitchen.

The biggest contribution to reducing the waste mountain of course comes from the fact that I use waste wood from my neighbourhood, as I mentioned, for the wood-burner. In addition to cutting the energy wasted taking it to the dump and the fact it provides me with carbon-neutral heating, it avoids the danger of the wood rotting anaerobically at the dump and emitting methane. Reducing my waste is really a state of mind that refuses as far as possible to buy things with unrecyclable packaging and that avoids throwaway goods. This again has produced an amusing interaction with the local council. Laudably, they have recently moved to making it compulsory to recycle your waste or face a £75 fine. However, as I often only need to put out my recycling bin about once a month, this means I am now receiving notices that claim I am not recycling and I face a fine if I do not! Naturally it will not happen, but this slight hassle is a small price to pay for getting the wider community to stop dumping recyclable materials.

Transport

I have never owned a car, so have not had to cut my carbon emissions from driving. Whilst I got my driving licence at 17, I have since allowed it to lapse. I usually cycle to my appointments around London. If I was working out of London, my clients used to collect me from the train station, but now I have a really cool new fold-up cycle and so have reduced the number of times I have to do this. It is really easy to take on the train. Flying was probably the one area where I was slow to really understand the climate impact. It is hard to believe that one flight to the west coast of the US can produce as many emissions as an entire household for nearly a third of a year. My main summer break this year was a yoga holiday in a small town outside Paris and so I was able to travel by Eurostar. I flew twice to Ireland for work and to see relatives. This amounted to 0.2 tonnes, so with my 0.1-tonne credit from the house, it means my annual energy carbon footprint for my house, car and flights for the last year came to 0.1 tonne, which was below my target of half a tonne.

So, having exceeded my goal of a carbon-neutral home and now having a carbon-negative one, it is fair to ask whether this cost a fortune. Over the last 15 years I have made the following major investments:

Solar electricity: £13,000
Solar hot water: £3,000
Wind turbine: £3,000
Wood-burner: £2,700
Rain harvester: £300
Total: £22,000

On the other hand my annual utility bills this year came to £93, most of which was the standing charge for my water supply. The RAC this year estimates that the average family car costs £5,500 per year to keep on the road. Over 15 years that amounts to a whopping £84,000 saved. So for me, having an eco-friendly lifestyle has not only made ethical and moral sense but has also made good financial sense. When the odd media interviewer suggests I was over-enthusiastic with my investments, I point out that £22,000 is still far less than the first year depreciation of £27,000 on a premium 4x4 BMW! It seems obvious to me that I am the better investor.

I've done it, so anyone can – including you!

Whether you have bought this book to eco-audit your own home, the houses on your street, the flats in your housing estate, the company you work for or that you own, your contribution is vitally important. If we can get every home and business in Britain eco-audited over the next five years, professionally or on a voluntary basis, it could result in millions of people realizing that saving the planet is often a matter of good house keeping. Individually, we can all make a significant contribution to the change that is so urgently needed. Millions of tonnes could be slashed from Britain's carbon dioxide emissions if we successfully do this.

If there is not a group already active in your community, set up one and use this book to act as your manual. If there is a group already tackling the climate crisis in your community join them and suggest they train community eco-auditors and, using this book as their handbook, try and get every home and business in your community eco-audited. Alternatively, if you own a business, why not encourage your staff to eco-audit their homes using this book after you have eco-audited your business. The same applies to schools. Make eco-auditing fundamental to how you run your school and then get the kids to eco-audit their own family homes or even, properly supervised, to eco-audit their street. There is no end to the range of uses that this book can be put to, especially given your imagination and enthusiasm.

So, ensure that you make your own life as eco-friendly as possible. Your family, friends and colleagues will appreciate your integrity and get eco-auditing themselves! Eco-audit your own home, your workplace, your neighbours' homes. Get other companies to eco-audit. Start an eco-auditing group in your neighbourhood and keep at it until you have ticked off every single house as having been done. There is absolutely no time to be lost. With a shocking quarter of the entire Arctic summer ice-field disappearing in the summer of 2007, we truly are now in the middle of the most urgent crisis humanity has ever faced. There is not a day to be wasted.

Oh, and one last thing: please do not forget to enjoy yourself. This is a gentle eco-revolution. Saving the planet is urgent, but it can also be fun and truly rewarding. Good luck!

Appendices

Resources

The following list of contacts will be useful for inclusion where relevant in drawing up your eco-audit report.

Basic information

Carbon calculator
National Energy Foundation:
www.nef.org.uk/energyadvice/co2calculator.htm

Carbon offsetting
www.carbonneutral.com

Eco-auditing
3 Acorns Eco-Audits: www.3acorns.co.uk

Building and maintenance

Building materials
www.ecomerchant.co.uk (for eco-friendly building materials)
www.thegreenbuildingstore.co.uk (for eco-friendly building materials)

Building professionals
Association for Environment Conscious Building: www.aecb.net

Paints
www.ecospaints.com

Cleaning

Cleaning products
www.biodegradable.biz
Clear Spring cleaning products are available from a range
of sources
www.e-cloth.com (for cleaning cloths that do not require
scouring creams or powders)
www.towntalk-polish.co.uk

Damp control
www.schrijversystem.com

Dry-cleaning
www.greenearth.co.uk

Toothbrushes and kitchen brushes with replaceable heads
www.naturalcollection.com

Cosmetics

Organic cosmetics
www.naturalcollection.com

Energy saving

Boilers
www.sedbuk.com (boiler efficiency database)

Chimney balloons
www.chimney-balloon.co.uk

Electric light bulbs
www.bltdirect.co.uk
www.commercial-lamps.co.uk
www.ebulbshop.com (for a wide range, including very small
   bulbs and halogen-fitting bulbs)
www.lightbulbs-direct (for a smaller range but very cheap bulbs)
www.megamanuk.com (for a small range of dimmable bulbs,
   including CFL halogen-fitting bulbs)

Electricity suppliers
www.good-energy.co.uk

Energy saving
www.standbybuster.com (for remote control stand-by turn-off)

Insulation
www.energysavingtrust.co.uk (insulation grants for home
   owners)
www.greenplanetinsulation.co.uk (suppliers of Warmcel,
   natural loft insulation)

Radiators
www.proeco.co.uk (radiator reflection insulation panels)

Energy – generating your own eco-energy

Accredited installers
www.lowcarbonbuildings.org.uk

Advice
Energy Saving Trust: www.energysavingtrust.org.uk

Grants
www.lowcarbonbuildings.org.uk
www.solarforlondon.org.uk (London grant scheme)

Heating
Heating Equipment Testing and Approval Scheme:
    www.hetas.co.uk

Solar energy
www.cel-f-solar.com (solar hot water for swimming
    pools)
www.chilternfutureenergy.co.uk (solar installations)
Solar Trade Asociation: www.greenenergy.co.uk
www.sundog-energy.co.uk (solar installations)

Wind energy
British Wind Energy Association: www.bwea.com
www.dti.gov.uk (wind-speed database)
www.dti.gov.uk/energy/sources/renewables/
    renewables-explained/wind-energy/page27708.html
    (wind speeds in UK)
www.eclectic-energy.co.uk (wind turbines – DC, yacht and
    domestic)
www.provenenergy.co.uk (wind turbines – small to medium-
    sized wind)

Wood-burners
www.clearviewstoves.com (wood-burning stoves)
www.ecofan.co.uk (wood-burner operated room fan)
www.ecofirst.net (wood-burning central heating boilers)

www.logpile.co.uk (wood suppliers for wood-burners by
    postcode)
www.stoves-are-us.co.uk (wood-burning stoves)

Shopping

Architectural salvage
www.salvo.co.uk

Clothes
www.greenfibres.co.uk

Curtains
www.thecurtainexchange.net (luxury reuse curtain shop chain)

Food
Marine Conservation Society: www.fishonline.org
Marine Stewardship Council: www.msc.org
www.vegboxschemes.co.uk (organic box scheme locator)

Products made from recycled materials
www.recycledproducts.org.uk

Second-hand objects
www.ebay.com
www.ebay.co.uk
www.freecycle.org

Shops
www.thegoodshoppingguide.co.uk (Listings of UK ethical
    companies, including an ethical rating)
www.ecocentric.co.uk (online eco-shop)

Stationery supplies
www.greenstat.co.uk
www.so3.co.uk

Transport

Cars
Bio-diesel: www.celticbiodiesel.co.uk
www.dft.gov.uk/ActOnCO2 (CO_2 emissions for cars currently
   on UK market)
Environmental Transport Association: www.eta.co.uk
www.vcacarfueldata.org.uk (car fuel data)

Rail
www.eurostar.com (trains to Europe from the UK)
www.raileurope.co.uk (European rail tickets)
www.seat61.com (European rail travel advice)

Responsible travel
www.responsible-travel.org
World Land Trust: www.carbonbalanced.org

Waste and recycling

Architectural salvage
www.salvo.co.uk

Composting
www.greencone.com (vermin-proof composting bins that also
   take food waste)

Government information

www.envirowise.gov.uk (agency to help companies cut waste)

www.netregs.gov.uk (regulations on waste)

Recycling

www.freecycle.org (surplus items for free)

www.recycle-more.co.uk (work- and home-based recycling)

www.recyclenow.com (for information about what your local
recycling collection will take by postcode)

www.envocare.co.uk (for recycling advice)

www.recycledproducts.org.uk (UK directory of recycled
products)

Reusable nappies

www.wen.org.uk

Reusable silicone sanitary products

www.mooncup.co.uk

Stopping junk mail

www.mpsonline.org.uk

Waste materials

www.wasteexchange.net (for companies sourcing waste
materials and for advertising their waste materials)

Water

Aerating shower heads

www.aqualogic-wc.com

Grey-water diverters
www.enviro-friendly.com

Plastic-cup recycling
www.save-a-cup.co.uk

Rain-harvesting systems
www.rainharvesting.co.uk
UK Rainwater Harvesting Association: www.ukrha.org

Water butts
www.waterbuttsdirect.co.uk

Water efficiency
www.waterefficientsolutions.net
UK government's water-efficient product list:
www.eco-water.gov.uk

Waterless urinals
www.watersolutions.com

Wildlife

Bat Conservation Trust: www.bats.org.uk
Royal Society for the Protection of Birds: www.rspb.org.uk
Wildlife Trusts: www.wildlifetrusts.org
World Wide Fund: www.wwf.org.uk

Eco-audit form

Building energy use

Electricity

- First meter reading
- Reading a year later
- Subtract final reading from first for total kWh for year (*UK average = 5,200 kWh*)
- Multiply by 0.43 for kg CO_2 emitted
- Divide by 1,000 for tonnes CO_2 emitted

Answer 1

Gas

- First meter reading
- Reading a year later
- Subtract final reading from first for total kWh for year (*UK average 33,500 kWh*)
- Multiply by 0.19 for kg CO_2 emitted
- Divide by 1,000 for tonnes CO_2 emitted

Answer 2a

Heating oil

- Total litres of heating oil used per year (*UK average 2,000 litres*)
- Multiply by 2.68 for kg CO_2 emitted
- Divide by 1,000 for tonnes CO_2 emitted

Answer 2b

Coal

- Total tonnes of coal used per year

  (*UK average 2.5 tonnes*)

- Multiply by 2.457 for kg CO_2 emitted

- Divide by 1,000 for tonnes CO_2 emitted

  Answer 2c

Total energy carbon footprint

- Add together answers 1 and 2

  Answer A

Car fuel

To calculate the number of tonnes of CO_2 that you've emitted by driving, use *one* of the following three methods.

Method 1: To calculate using total fuel used in a year

- Total litres of petrol/diesel used for year

- Multiply by 2.68 for kg CO_2

  emitted (1.5 for LPG)

- Divide by 1,000 for tonnes CO_2 emitted

  Answer 3

Method 2: To calculate using total distance driven in kilometres in a year

- Total kilometres driven for year

  (*UK average = 13,920 kilometres*)

- Multiply by 0.23 for kg CO_2 emitted

- Divide by 1,000 for tonnes CO_2 emitted

  Answer 3

Method 3: To calculate using total distance driven in miles in a year

- Total miles driven for year
  (UK average = 8,700 miles)

- Multiply by 0.36 for kg CO_2 emitted

- Divide by 1,000 for tonnes CO_2 emitted

Answer 3

Total carbon footprint for energy and car use

- Add together answers 1, 2 and 3

Answer B

Flights

- Number of short-haul return flights (e.g. London–Paris, London–Edinburgh)

- Multiply by 0.2 tonnes

Answer 4

- Number of medium-haul return flights (e.g. Edinburgh–Ankara, Cardiff–Cairo)

- Multiply by 0.8 tonnes

Answer 5

- Number of medium- to long-haul return flights (e.g. Belfast–South Africa, London–Japan)

- Multiply by 2 tonnes

Answer 6

- Number of long-haul return flights (e.g. Edinburgh–New Zealand)

- Multiply by 4.2 tonnes

Answer 7

Total carbon footprint for flying

- Add together answers 4, 5, 6 and 7

Answer C

Total direct energy carbon footprint

- Add together answers B and C

Water

- First meter reading

- Reading a year later

- Subtract final reading from first for total cubic metres for year

- Multiply by 1,000 for litres

- Divide by number of adult equivalents to get personal water usage and then by 365 to get average daily usage in litres (*London average is 160 litres per person per day*)

Rubbish

- Number of black bags/wheelie bins of non-recyclable rubbish produced each week (*Average UK household produces one wheelie bin per week or 1.1 tonnes per year*)

Food

- Portions of meat consumed per week

- Multiply by 52 for annual number of portions (*Average UK person consumes 1kg meat per week*)

Example home eco-audit report

Address
London household
EN5

Introduction
From the rough figures that you gave me for the house it appears that your home's annual energy consumption results in the emission of about 22 tonnes of CO_2 per annum. This is almost four times the national average of 6.2 tonnes per home. This does not include any figures for flights or driving. Your full energy carbon footprint can be calculated by inputting the figures in the eco-audit form below or in the attached Excel spreadsheet.

The average total CO_2 emissions per person, including all sources of CO_2, is 9.5 tonnes per annum in the UK and in my opinion the climate crisis is so urgent that we all need to aim for a global average of about 1 tonne per person per annum. The global average currently is about 3.75 tonnes.

The following are my recommendations for the steps you need to take in order to improve your home's environmental performance and to help you start the process of achieving this goal.

Renewables

Green tariff
It would be excellent if you switched to a green electricity supplier that sources all its electricity from zero-carbon sources such as

hydro power, wind power and solar panels. Good Energy (www.good-energy.co.uk) and Ecotricity (www.ecotricity.co.uk) are considered to have the best green energy standards. In one easy hit this would remove *all* your CO_2 emissions from your electricity use. Ecotricity pledge to match the price of your regional electricity supplier and Good Energy is about 10 per cent more expensive than usual suppliers. All you need to do is to go to one of their websites and fill in the relevant details from your current electricity bill.

On-site renewable energy

The roof of your swimming pool looks suitable for the installation of a solar hot-water system. As the water temperature required for a swimming pool is not as high as that for household heating systems, solar hot-water systems can work well for swimming pools in the summer months requiring little back-up. An average-sized system for a swimming pool currently costs about £10,000. A small grant of £400 is available through the Low Carbon Buildings Programme (www.lowcarbonbuildings.org). Cel-F Solar Systems (www.cel-f-solar.com) have experience installing solar hot-water systems for swimming pools.

Domestic solar thermal (hot-water) systems cost from £2,500–£5,000. Grants of £400 are available from the Low Carbon Buildings Programme for domestic systems. Additional grants are available from some local councils in London under the Solar for London programme. The systems are cheaper if you have a header tank system rather than a mains-pressure water system. Chiltern Future Energy (www.chilternfutureenergy.co.uk) and Southern Solar (www.southernsolar.co.uk) will both do a free site assessment and provide quotations for your home for solar hot-water and solar electric systems.

For further information and a list of suppliers visit the Energy Saving Trust website (www.energysavingtrust.org.uk).

Wood-burning central heating systems

You should consider having a wood-powered automatically fed central heating system. This would be a carbon-neutral option. Your garage would be an ideal location for a wood-powered boiler as it offers a good storage area for the wood.

The cost of these boilers depends on your choice of system. A typical 15-kW pellet boiler (the average size required for a three-bedroom semi-detached house) costs around £5,000–£11,000 installed, including the cost of the flue and commissioning. A manual log-feed system of the same size is slightly cheaper.

Information on suppliers and grants for wood-pellet or log central heating systems is available at the Energy Saving Trust website (www.energysavingtrust.org.uk). A grant of £1,500 is available from the Low Carbon Buildings Programme (www.lowcarbon buildings.org).

Wood-burners and wood-burning boilers have to be installed by HETAS-regulated installers (www.hetas.co.uk). Wood Energy Ltd (www.woodenergyltd.co.uk) is one of the UK's leading wood boiler installers.

Information on local wood suppliers is available by typing in your post code at the National Energy Foundation's log pile website (www.nef.org.uk/logpile/fuelsuppliers/index.htm).

Water meter

You are already on a water meter, which means that you are financially and environmentally accountable for your water use. It also means that you will benefit financially from any investment in water efficiency.

Curtains

Curtains should be well lined or, even better, thermally lined. It is important to ensure that curtains do not hang over any radiators when drawn because this allows the heat to escape through the windows instead of heating the room. It is a good idea to place Velcro on the curtains and on the adjacent walls so that you can seal off the windows and keep the heat in at night.

At present you do not have curtains in the nanny flat, the office or on any of the downstairs windows in the house. You should consider having some fitted.

Good quality reuse curtains can often be found on eBay (www.ebay.co.uk) or at The Curtain Exchange (www.thecurtain exchange.net). The Curtain Exchange have stores in Dulwich and Hammersmith.

Doors

Open-plan issues

The house is totally open plan downstairs, which means that you are heating large unoccupied areas of the house unnecessarily. You should consider fitting thermally lined curtains so that you have the option of partitioning off the living room, dining room and kitchen areas when they are not in use. This would reduce the area to be heated in winter.

Alternatively you could consider installing doors or glass partitions so that you can separate off the living room, the dining room and the piano room in winter as necessary.

Unused rooms with doors

In winter turn off the radiators in rooms that you are not using and close the doors if they have them.

Insulation

Roof insulation

Your roof space has 1980s standard insulation. This should be upgraded by topping it up to modern insulation standards.

The existing insulating material is in need of repair because much of it was ripped away to make room for the installation of the halogen lamps. You should get a quote for doubling the overall insulation to a minimum depth of 300mm – but the more the better – including the hatches and also for the installation of boxes around the halogen light fittings, which is required by fire regulations.

The ceiling of the garage also needs to be insulated as it is under the dining-room floor.

Most utility companies have schemes to help you upgrade or install roof and cavity wall insulation. Check your own utility company website for details of any current special offers. Alternatively visit the Energy Saving Trust website (www.energysavingtrust.org.uk/proxy/view/full/2019/grantsand offerssearch) for a full list of insulation and efficiency grants available to people living in your area. Simply type your postcode into the grant search box and you will get a list of offers and grants available in your area.

There are a number of eco-friendly alternatives to mineral wool insulation provided by the above schemes. These include Warmcel spray-in insulation, which is made from mineralized recycled paper. Warmcel is particularly good for difficult spaces as it can be sprayed in. Warmcel was judged the best available insulation in a recent *Which?* survey.

Other alternatives include Thermafleece, which is made from waste sheep-shearing products, and FSC certified wood-fibre insulation boarding. There is also a natural insulation material made from flax that is available from Construction Resources (www.constructionresources.com).

Windows

One of the windows in the nanny flat is cracked and will need to be repaired.

Doors

The letter box in the front door is in need of repair. There is a strong draught through it at present.

The front door to the nanny flat needs to be fitted with strip insulation and the keyhole should be fitted with a keyhole flap.

The wooden door to the swimming pool needs to be fitted with strip insulation and the keyhole needs to be sealed.

The door to the lobby of the gym is in need of repair. An insulation brush should also be fitted at the bottom of this door.

The garage doors are very draughty and need draught sealers.

The keyhole in the door between the garage and the house needs to be sealed.

Heating

Central heating

Your central heating is set at 32°C in winter, which is extremely high. Try setting it at the recommended background setting of 19°C instead and see if this is sufficient for your needs. Every degree above 19°C adds 10 per cent to your gas bill. Thus having it set at 32°C uses 120 per cent more energy than the recommended background temperature setting.

It is understandable that your partner, who is used to much warmer temperatures due to being from a much warmer country, will want a higher temperature than is recommended for the UK, but try and avoid having the whole house heated to accommodate this. Instead, I suggest that you identify one room that can be heated to a warmer temperature for evening use.

You should also experiment with different timings to see if you can reduce the number of hours that you use your central heating. Ideally it should be set to come on half an hour before you get up and to go off an hour before you go to bed, with an appropriate gap during the day.

Ensure the system is on a seven-day timer, as you will probably have different requirements at weekends.

Underfloor heating boiler

The underfloor heating boiler is set at 9, which is the setting for severe winter cold. Try turning it down to 3, 4 or 5 and see if this is sufficient for your needs.

Wood-burning stove

You have a coal-effect gas fire in the living room. These are one of the most inefficient and highest CO_2 emitters of any heating system. Over 85 per cent of the gas and heat is wasted up the chimney. You should consider installing a wood-burning stove instead.

Wood-burning stoves are a carbon-neutral source of warmth. Modern glass-fronted stoves retain all the ambience of an open fire and are up to four times more efficient than open wood fires. You will need to ensure the stove is a model that is compatible with any local smoke-free-zone regulations.

Information about wood-burning stoves can be found at the Clearview Stoves website (www.clearviewstoves.com). Stoves cost up to £3,000 installed. Unfortunately, there are no grants for such wood-burning stoves unless they are automatically fed wood-pellet stoves.

If you do decide to have a wood stove, you should also purchase an Ecofan (www.ecofan.co.uk). The Caframo Ecofan is a heat-powered fan designed to circulate the warm air created by a wood stove. This fan does not use any batteries or mains electricity but simply the heat from the stove to power it. It costs about £60.

Flueless gas fires

Alternatively you could consider replacing the coal-effect gas fire with a flueless gas fire.

Flueless gas fires are fitted with catalytic converters, which eliminate the need for a flue. They are 100 per cent efficient, converting 100 per cent of the gas into heat energy, compared with between 10–15 per cent for open coal-effect gas fires! They are only recommended for homes with large rooms with background central heating, such as yours, because they add some condensation.

Flueless gas fires cost in the region of £500, not including installation, and come in a range of styles. These styles include modern minimalist wall-mounted designs that would fit in very well with your current décor. Burley Appliances (www.burley.co.uk) provide flueless coal-effect gas fires.

The added advantage of both a wood-burner and the flueless gas fire in this situation, is that both would involve the sealing up of the chimney draught, through which you are currently losing significant amounts of your central heating warmth in winter.

Chimney balloons

If you decide not to install either a wood-burning stove or a flueless gas fire then you could install a professional chimney balloon, which would stop you losing a considerable amount of heat up your chimney when the central heating is on. These are available from Chimney Balloon (www.chimney-balloon.co.uk) and cost about £20 each. They are really only suitable for fireplaces that are unused or rarely used.

Radiator reflector panels

Reflector insulation panels should be fitted throughout the house behind all radiators that are on outside walls, for example in the office, the nanny flat, the guest room, both the children's bedrooms and the swimming pool. This is because up to 30 per cent of a radiator's heat can be lost through the adjacent outside wall. These panels are easily installed and will reflect the heat into the room rather than allowing it to leak into the wall behind it. They are available in most large DIY stores or from Shop Eco (www.shopeco.co.uk) and cost about £8 per radiator.

Radiators by windows

Some of your radiators are situated directly under windows, for instance in the office and the children's bedrooms, thus losing much of their heat through the glass above. This can be corrected by installing a shelf above the radiator and attaching insulation underneath the shelf to direct the warm air away from the window and into the room.

Hot water

Your hot-water boiler is set at 80°C, which is very high. Lower it to the recommended setting of 60°C. As the average temperature for a shower is about 39°C, you will not have to add so much cold water to make it comfortable. **This is an urgent item.**

As with your central heating system, you should experiment with the timings of your hot-water system to see if you can reduce the number of hours that it is switched on. At present your main house system is set to come on at 5.30 a.m. and to switch off at 1.00 a.m. Try setting it to come on between 6.00 and 9.00 a.m. and then again between 6.00 and 9.00 p.m. instead. This would save up to 13½ hours of heating per day. **This is an urgent item**.

Again, consider putting the system on a seven-day timer to allow for your different requirements at weekends.

The hot water in the nanny flat is turned on 24 hours a day. You should have the system checked by an engineer to find out how to turn it off when the flat is not in use. **This is an urgent item.**

Swimming pool

Experiment with the controls of the swimming pool to see if you can reduce the number of hours that it is switched on and still satisfy your needs. Check with the swimming pool company to see what its recommended minimum timings are.

Rain harvester

Your house looks suitable for a rain-harvesting system. General information on large, professional rain-harvesting systems is available from the UK Rainwater Harvesting Association's website (www.ukrha.org).

Envir-Eau (www.envireau.com) are manufacturers and installers of such systems. They cost from about £3,000 upwards. The systems are often buried in the garden and use a small electric pump.

Rainharvesting Systems (www.rainharvesting.co.uk) have a new system available that would not require a large hole to be dug as the water tanks could be located in your garage. They cost from £750 upwards plus installation.

Shower

Ensure that your showers are fitted with aerating shower heads that mix air and water to increase efficiency by up to 30 per cent without decreasing effectiveness. You are already planning to install a new shower in the nanny flat but the shower heads in the children's bathroom and the en-suite bathrooms in the main bedroom and the guest bedroom also need to be replaced.

Hansgrohe (www.hansgrohe.co.uk) do some elegant aerating shower heads, costing about £30. The Aquabrand website (www.aquabrand.com) sells Hansgrohe raindance and raindance AIR hand showers.

Toilets

If you decide to install a new toilet in the nanny flat, choose the most water-efficient model on the market. Dual-flush versions using as little as 2.5 litres are now available.

There is a dual-flush toilet in the children's bathroom. Check with your children to make sure that they know how it works.

Install an Interflush (www.interflush.co.uk) device in the toilet in the swimming-pool room. This will enable it to only flush for as long as you hold the handle down. These devices are slightly complicated to install so you might need a plumber to install it, although they are supposedly DIY.

To save water, place a water-filled plastic bottle, brick or water-hippo in the swimming-pool toilet water tank. If it continues to work well, experiment with adding a second and see if it still works well. Modern toilets use only 6 litres for a full flush, whereas older toilets use 9 litres for every flush.

Taps

If you replace taps in rooms other than the kitchen or bathroom, ensure that they are fitted with flow regulators and spray nozzles to save water.

Energy-saving light bulbs

You could reduce the total wattage used by the bulbs in your home substantially by replacing all the non-energy saving light bulbs with energy-saving ones. These can be bought at any large DIY store or online.

In particular, the light bulbs in the following lights need to be replaced:
- the lights in the nanny flat;
- the staircase chandelier;
- the lights in the swimming-pool toilet;
- the lamp in the main bedroom;
- the two fittings in the en-suite bathroom of the main bedroom;
- the pendant lamps in both the children's bedrooms;
- the lights in the utility room (two energy-saving bulbs here would use only 11 watts).

A 20-watt energy-saving bulb gives the same light as a traditional 100-watt bulb. An 11-watt energy-saving bulb gives the same light as a traditional 60-watt bulb. A 7-watt energy-saving bulb gives same light as a traditional 40-watt bulb.

The down-lighters in the entrance hall use 750 watts. Try to avoid down-lighters, which are inherently inefficient, unless considering using LEDs. No energy-efficient lamps to date work on low voltage transformer systems, so avoid these at all costs. Although Osram have just brought out a range of slightly more efficient halogen bulbs.

The up-lighters in the entrance hall are also very energy wasteful at 200–300 watts per lamp.

The lighting in the kitchen uses a very high total of 1,600 watts. In contrast, my entire two-bedroom house is lit with 190 watts in total. You should consider getting some standard lamps with energy-saving bulbs instead.

The overhead lamp in the office uses a very high 300-watt bulb. Consider using a standard lamp with energy-saving bulbs here as well.

Consider putting a high wattage energy-saving bulb in the main lamp in the gym and using that light rather than the halogen lights you are using at present. You could get a lampshade if the bulb looks too bare.

You are using large Edison 80-watt screw-in bulbs in the swimming pool. Check the ebulbshop website (www.ebulbshop.com) and see if you can find an energy-saving alternative.

Energy-saving light bulbs now come in a range of styles to fit most requirements, including candle-bulbs and bulbs that fit halogen fittings and use 7 watts each rather than 40–50 watts each. Note that 7-watt compact fluorescent lamps (CFLs) that fit halogen fittings only work at normal voltages, that is those that don't require transformers. Experiment with one to see if it will work on your system and if you like the light it provides.

A wide range of energy-saving bulbs, including small bulbs and halogen fittings and LED bulbs, is available from ebulbshop (www.ebulbshop.com), BLT Direct (www.bltdirect.co.uk) and Commercial Lamp Supplies (www.commercial-lamps.co.uk). A smaller range, including very cheap bulbs, is available from Lightbulbs Direct (www.lightbulbs-direct.com). A small range of dimmable bulbs is available at Megaman (www.megamanuk.com).

You mentioned that you had attempted to get a quote from a natural light tube installer without success. You could try Sunpipe (www.sunpipe.co.uk) who do domestic and commercial systems.

Fridges and deep-freezers

You should experiment with the thermostats in your kitchen fridge and deep-freezer to find the optimum temperature settings for your needs. At present your kitchen fridge is set at 4°C. Ideally it should be set at 5°C. Your deep-freezer is set at - 20°C and the optimum setting is -16°C.

You have a second fridge/freezer for drinks in the utility room. You should consider whether this is essential or whether you could rationalize your usage so that the drinks fridge can be turned off. This is important as fridges are one of the largest consumers of household electricity because they are switched on 24 hours a day, all year round. If you decide to keep the drinks fridge, the setting could at least be turned down to 1.

Check whether SavaPlugs are needed for the fridges. These help to regulate the electricity used by the fridge motors and can also provide up to 20 per cent savings on electricity use. Email the savawatt.com website at info@savawatt.com to find out if your fridge needs one. You can also find a list of fridge models that do not benefit from the use of a SavaPlug at www.savaplug.co.uk.

You should also ensure that you clean the back coils of the fridges once a year (clear the fluff!) to ensure continuing efficient operation. A hoover will do this in seconds.

If you replace your fridge/freezers, ensure that the new models have the best energy rating possible (AAA or green colour coding).

Replacement electrical goods

Ensure that any other new electrical goods that you buy have the best energy rating possible (AAA or green colour coding).

Ask about the wattage of sets if buying a new television. Plasma screens use twice as much electricity as cathode screens.

If you buy a new washing machine or dishwasher, ensure that you choose a model that can take a hot feed so that it can take advantage of a solar hot-water system.

Stand-by

Try not to leave appliances and gadgets on stand-by – always turn them off completely when you have finished with them. In particular, ensure that phone-chargers, broadband connections and so on are turned off when they are not in use. There were a large number of electrical appliances on stand-by during my visit, including:

- the computer for the TV and sub-woofer (15 watts);
- the TV in the kitchen (16 watts);
- the hoover charger (15 watts);
- the cross trainer and TV in the gym;
- the cupboard with the audio and TV equipment.

You should consider getting a Standby Buster for all the TV and audio equipment in the living room cupboard and, indeed, for all your other stand-by equipment. I came across this device after my visit to your house and have trialled it at home and been delighted with it. As long as each socket has a receiving device then a single hand-held remote control will turn off all the stand-by devices programmed to receive its signal. It even has the capacity to turn off different sections of the house as required. You can purchase one from www.standbybuster.com.

The kitchen TV should be turned off at the wall switch when it is not in use.

The cross trainer and TV in the gym should be switched off when they are not in use.

The computer, printer and Wi-Fi in the office are currently left switched on at night. You could turn them off when you go to bed and also when they are not in use during the day.

If a gadget or adaptor feels hot to touch when it is not in use then this means that it is using up to 5 watts continuously. This is not much but over an entire year, and with millions doing the same, it adds up significantly.

Cars

Your cars are:

• a Volvo Diesel XC 90;

• a Jaguar XK;

• a Mini Cooper.

You should use the Mini Cooper in preference to the other two cars where possible because it has a much better CO_2 emissions rating. The Jaguar will emit about 100 per cent more emissions than the Mini per kilometre and the Volvo about 65 per cent more.

You can find information about the CO_2 emissions per kilometre for all current car models at the DVLA website (www.vcacarfueldata.org.uk).

If or when changing your car it is important to be aware that even within the same class of car the emissions can vary by up to 40 per cent.

Cosmetics

Consider organic chemical-free alternatives when buying cosmetics. Ranges are available from Natural Collection (www.naturalcollection.com).

Bed linen

When replacing bedlinen you should buy organic cotton sheets because cotton production accounts for over 25 per cent of total pesticide use worldwide. Ranges are available at Natural Collection (www.naturalcollection.com). You should also seek to avoid white bedlinen and towels that need to be washed at far higher temperatures than coloured ones.

Food

You should consider ordering organic fruit, potatoes, eggs and bread through your local organic box scheme. You can find a list of local suppliers by typing your postcode into the www.vegboxschemes.co.uk website. Details of where to buy Marine Stewardship Council fish can be found on their website at www.msc.org.

Cleaning supplies

A wide range of chemical-free cleaning products is available at Natural Collection (www.naturalcollection.com). They also supply products from Bio-D, which offers a British version of Ecover products made from organic materials.

You should replace plastic soap containers with soap on a magnetic holder. This will reduce the amount of packaging you throw away and also reduce the mess on the sink. You can purchase magnetic soap holders from Philip Morris & Son (www.philipmorris.uk.com). Try to avoid using anti-bacterial soap unless really necessary. Anti-bacterial products in non-clinical situations unnecessarily increase the danger of antibiotic resistance.

Plastic waste reduction

Reduce plastic waste by buying replaceable kitchen brush handles and replaceable toothbrush head handles. These are available at Natural Collection (www.naturalcollection.com).

Carbon offsetting

If you aim to be carbon neutral in terms of your household energy consumption, you could consider using carbon offsetting. Simply type in last year's usage into the calculator at the CarbonNeutral Company website (www.carbonneutral.com) and it will tell you the cost of offsetting this amount of CO_2. The CarbonNeutral Company invest in planting forests, renewable energy and energy efficiency projects in developing countries that either absorb CO_2 or reduce CO_2 emissions in the first place.

Wine

Finally, to celebrate your new even more eco-friendly home, visit the Soil Association website (www.soilassociation.org/web/sa/saweb.nsf/Living/wine.html) for information and contacts about English organic wines!

Next steps

Keep this report as a checklist to monitor your progress. Put a date in your diary for six months time as the date to revisit this checklist and review the progress that you have made.

Remember, it is important to note positive progress in order to maintain momentum and commitment to continuous improvement.

Keeping an annual track of water, gas, electric and waste consumption can really help motivate your improvements. An environmental lifestyle is a process, not an immediate outcome! The attached eco-audit form may help you keep a record of this and help you see your positive progress. I have attached an Excel version in case you find that easier to use, as it will do the calculations automatically for you.

Good luck!
Donnachadh McCarthy, 3 Acorns Eco-Audits
September 2007

Index

Acknowledgements

First and foremost thanks to Sandra Rigby, my commissioning editor at Gaia for having the faith that I could produce another eco-book of worth and for her patience in the face of my endless suggestions about design, cover and title!! To Clare Churly for being such a gentle editor and for her many helpful corrections and clarifications of the original manuscript. Thanks also to Nicholas and Liz Cass-Beggs, Joseph Corbett, Richard Griffiths, Cathy Priddey, Iarla Kilbane-Dawe and Matthew Hendrickson, for their invaluable help and support with making 3 Acorns Eco-audits so successful.

To Clare Thomas and John Merivale at the City Bridge Trust who gave me my first big break into organizational eco-auditing, when they put their trust in me to carry out a major ground-breaking charity eco-auditing project for them. Gratitude is also due to Christian Broughton and Louisa Saunders and my other *Independent* newspaper editors whose commissions financially enabled me to devote the time required to writing this book and also to Emma Manning, editor of *Dance Europe* (the world's best ballet magazine!) for giving me my first substantial break as a professional writer. Thanks are also due to Julia Stephenson for all her generous moral and media support.

Finally a debt of thanks is also due to all my eco-auditing clients, domestic and commercial, who not only financially enable me to devote my time to spreading the word on how to take constructive action to halt our environmental destruction, but also act as invaluable teachers for me along the way and without whom this book would not have been possible. Let us hope we are in time.

Donnachadh McCarthy
Peckham, October 2007

Executive Editor Sandra Rigby
Managing Editor Clare Churly
Executive Art Editor Leigh Jones
Illustrations Carroll Associates and BrindeauMexter
Page make-up Dorchester Typesetting Group Ltd
Senior Production Controller Simone Nauerth

Greening A Business

The Eco-Auditor Calls
(DVD or VHS) 2 FILM PACKAGE – 2007, 31+31 mins

Donnachadh McCarthy is an eco-auditor. He helps businesses who want to become environmentally sustainable. These two films describe his work with two very different organisations.

FILM 1: THE WHOLESALER (31 mins) EFG is a company that sells food and drinks to schools and hospitals. Their idealistic boss calls in Donnachadh to help them become "carbon neutral". Donnachadh examines every aspect of their business from the canteen fridge to the fuel in their vans. With the eco-auditor's help, EFG makes progress - but there's still a lot to do.

FILM 2: THE CHARITY (31 mins) Merton Voluntary Services Council is a charity which supports voluntary groups. Donnachadh is called in to help them become greener. Just changing where they put paper to be recycled makes a big difference. Sustainability is all about small details. But the building where they rent an office is a bigger challenge. It's not easy to persuade the building managers to change their energy-wasteful ways - but even here green progress is made.

DVD EXTRAS include a tour of an eco-house and in-depth interview with Donnachadh

Support Booklet also available.

For price and availability please contact:
TV Choice
PO Box 597
Bromley
Kent
BR2 0YB
Tel: (020) 8464 7402
Fax: (020) 8464 7845
Email: tvchoiceuk@aol.com
www.tvchoice.uk.com